PLUMBING CODE OF NEW YORK CITY

Guide and Interpretation

PLUMBING CODE
OF NEW YORK CITY
Guide and Interpretation

Samuel N. Lent

Chief Plumbing Inspector in the City of New York
New York University graduate in Plumbing Engineering
Licensed to teach by the
  New York City Board of Education
  New York State Board of Education
Licensed Master Plumber, New York City
Licensed Installer of Oil Burners, Class "A"
  in New York City
Member of the American Society of Sanitary Engineering

INDUSTRIAL PRESS INC.

200 Madison Ave., New York, N.Y. 10016

PLUMBING CODE OF NEW YORK CITY—Guide and Interpretation

Library of Congress Catalog Card Number LC 72-153471
ISBN 0-8311-1074-0

TABLE OF CONTENTS

PREFACE

The purpose of this book is to analyze the contents of the new City of New York Plumbing Code and to interpret this code in the most simple language possible. The numerous diagrams give a clear, pictorial explanation of the Articles in the Code.

Cross references are also made to the Articles and diagrams so that more complete information can be found about any desired item. Any of the Articles can be located easily in the following manner:

1. Check the Table of Contents
2. Find the correct Section number for the desired Definition or item in the Building Code or Reference Standard RS-16.

If a comparison is desired between any Article in this book and the official City of New York Building Code, refer to the Section numbers at the left, which are identical in both books.

Mention is frequently made to "Reference Standards." These are informative manuals published in the United States by national organizations. The booklets treat a "certain type of work" pertaining to the particular trade noted directly below the RS number.

Included in this volume is the complete "Department of Water Supply, Gas and Electricity Manual of Rules," with arrows inserted throughout, to point out the most important features. There is also an extensive appendix with TABLES TO BE USED TO DETERMINE THE SIZE OF SERVICE PIPES AND TAPS, methods for determining WATER DISTRIBUTION PIPE SIZES, and numerous important mathematical formulas concerned with plumbing work.

In addition, the book contains the following information printed in the City of New York Building Code:

Diagrammatic illustrations: Figures RS 16-1 to RS 16-13, Tables RS 16-1 to RS 16-28, and many Section numbers NOT containing plumbing information but which are related in some way to the plumbing business.

I would like to express my personal thanks to Mr. Harold A. Hand for his very valuable assistance in preparing this book. He has had many years of experience in Plumbing design, having been Plumbing Project Engineer for six years with Haines, Lundberg and Waehler, and for the past five years, Senior Mechanical Designer for Lockwood, Greene Engineers, Inc. My thanks also to Mr. Jeffrey Faro for his assistance; to my wife, Rita, for her patience and encouragement; to Mr. Holbrook H. Horton and Mrs. Clara Fried Zwiebel of the Industrial Press Inc., for their guidance in the editing and production of the book.

TITLE A–GENERAL PROVISIONS

§641-1.0   **Definitions.**–For the purposes of this chapter:

1. The term "multiple dwelling" shall mean such dwelling as defined by Section 4 of the Multiple Dwelling Law;

2. The term "building" shall mean any building, structure, premises, or part thereof;

3. The term "service equipment" shall mean equipment, and all components thereof, which provide sanitation, power, light, heat, ventilation, air-conditioning, refuse disposal, fire-fighting, transportation or other facilities for buildings.

TITLE B–LICENSES

ARTICLE 1

GENERAL PROVISIONS

§B26-1.0   **General license requirements.**–Including application, qualifications,
to   residence requirements and issuance by Commissioner of Buildings.
§B26-1.2
§B26-1.8   **Revocation of licenses.**–Commissioner has power to revoke license.

ARTICLE 2

MASTER PLUMBER LICENSE

§B26-2.0   **Requirement of license.**–Master Plumber license requirements have not changed for examination except for residence, and are now under the jurisdiction of the Department of Buildings instead of the Department of Health.

ARTICLE 3

WELDER LICENSE

§B26-3.0   **Requirement of license.**–

ARTICLE 4

HIGH-PRESSURE BOILER OPERATING ENGINEER LICENSE

§B26-4.0   **Requirement of license.**–
§B26-4.1   **Definition.**–Boiler having pressure over 15 psi of steam and rated over 10 hp or produces hot water at pressure of 160 psi or produces hot water at temperature over 250 degrees F.

ARTICLE 8

OIL-BURNING EQUIPMENT INSTALLER LICENSES

§B26-8.3   **Class "A" License.**–To install heavy fuel-oil jobs.
§B26-8.4   **Class "B" License.**–To install fuel oil No. 1 to No. 4 jobs. (Also see Section C26-1402.2.)

TITLE C, PART 1.—BUILDING CONSTRUCTION

ARTICLE 1

GENERAL PROVISIONS

§C26-11.0   **All new work to conform.**—(Also see Section C26-100.5.)
For work permitted under Old Code.—
(1) Permit can be filed within 12 months of effective date of this Code.
(2) Work must be started within 12 months.
(3) Work may be completed later.

ARTICLE 2

PERMITS

§C26-20.0   **Permit requirements.**—
§C26-21.0   **Approval of plans.**—
§C26-22.0   **Signature to permit.**—Permits to be approved by Building Department.

ARTICLE 3

FEES

§C26-30.0   **Requirement of fee.**—To be paid to Building Department.—
EXCEPTIONS.
§C26-31.0   **Fees for approval of plans and work permits.**—To be paid to Building Department. Total amounts, also separate fees.
§C26-32.0   **Computation of fees for work permits.**—To be paid to Building Department.—Required permit fee amounts for new buildings; building alterations; foundations and open spaces, etc.; demolition and removal; plumbing; signs; service equipment; fee refunds and alteration cost substantiations.
§C26-32.5   **Fees for plumbing permits.**—Computed in same manner as for alterations, except for plumbing less than $1000.00 per job, involving no structural change or change in Certificate of Occupancy. Check with department for current amount of fee.

ARTICLE 4

INSPECTIONS

§C26-40.0   **Right of entry for inspection.**—By Building Department Inspectors.—
§C26-41.0   **Inspections of Building work.**—

ARTICLE 5

CERTIFICATES OF OCCUPANCY

§C26-50.0   **Requirement of Certificate of Occupancy (C.O.).**—Shall be illegal to occupy building otherwise.

PART II, BUILDING CODE

ARTICLE 1

ADMINISTRATION AND ENFORCEMENT

TABLE OF CONTENTS

*"§C26-" omitted from Section numbers in this table.

*" §C26-" omitted from Section numbers in this table.

*" §C26-" omitted from Section numbers in this table.

*" §C26-" omitted from Section numbers in this table.

SUB-ARTICLE 100.0   GENERAL PROVISIONS

§C26-100.5   **Effective Date of Code.**—(Also see Section C26-11.0.) For work permitted under Old Code.—
    (1) Permit can be filed within 12 months of effective date of this Code.
    (2) Work must be started within 12 months.
    (3) Work may be completed later.

SUB-ARTICLE 103.0   ALTERATION OF EXISTING BUILDINGS

Subject to the provisions of Section 100.5, and except as otherwise specifically provided by the provisions of this Code, the following provisions shall apply to the alteration of existing buildings, whether made voluntarily or as a result of damage, deterioration, or other cause.

LOCAL LAWS OF THE CITY OF NEW YORK

FOR THE YEAR 1969, NO. 61.

A local law to amend the Administrative Code of the City of New York, in relation to clarifying and correcting provisions relating to the powers and duties of the Department of Buildings and incorporating certain fire-safety provisions of the Multiple Dwelling Law.

Be it enacted by the Council as follows:

Section 1. Sections C26-103.1, C26-103.2, C26-103.3 and C26-103.4 of the Administrative Code of the City of New York, as added by Local Law Number Seventy-six of the City of New York of the year nineteen hundred sixty-eight, are hereby amended to read as follows:

§C26-103.1 **Alterations exceeding 60 per cent of building value.**—If the cost of making alterations in any 12-month period shall exceed 60 per cent of the value of the building, the entire building shall be made to comply with the requirements of this Code, except as provided in Section C26-103.6.

§C26-103.2 **Alterations between 30 per cent and 60 per cent of building value.**—If the cost of making alterations in any 12-month period shall be between 30 per cent and 60 per cent of the value of the building, only those portions of the building altered shall be made to comply with the requirements of this Code, except as provided in Section C26-103.6.

§C26-103.3 **Alterations under 30 per cent of building value.**—Except as otherwise provided for in Section C26-103.6, if the cost of making alterations in any 12-month period shall be under 30 per cent of the value of the building, those portions of the building altered may, at the option of the owner, be altered in accordance with the requirements of this Code, or altered in compliance with the applicable laws in existence prior to December 6, 1968, provided the general safety and public welfare are not thereby endangered.

§C26-103.4 **Alterations involving change in occupancy or use.**—Except as otherwise provided for in Section C26-103.6, if the alteration of a building or space therein results in a change in the occupancy group classification of the building under the provisions of ARTICLE 3, then the entire building shall be made to comply with the requirements of this Code. If the alteration of a space in a building involves a change in the occupancy or use thereof, the alteration work involved in the change shall be made to comply with the requirements of this Code and the remaining portion of the building shall be altered to such an extent as may be necessary to protect the safety and welfare of the occupants.

§C26-103.5 **Alteration costs.**—Value of a building to be considered 1.25 times the current assessed valuation.

Section 2. SUB–ARTICLE 103.0 of Chapter 26 of such Code, as added by Local Law Number Seventy-six of the year nineteen hundred sixty-eight, is hereby amended by adding thereto a new Section, to be Section C26-103.6, to read as follows:

§C26-103.6 **Alterations to multiple dwellings and conversions to multiple dwellings.**—At the option of the owner, regardless of the cost of the alteration or conversion, an alteration may be made to a multiple dwelling or a building may be converted to a multiple dwelling in accordance with all requirements of this Code or in accordance with all applicable laws in existence prior to December 6, 1968, provided the general safety and public welfare are not thereby endangered.

Underlined portions of Section C26-104.3 are VERY IMPORTANT.

SUB-ARTICLE 104.0 MINOR ALTERATIONS: ORDINARY REPAIRS

§C26-104.1 **Minor alterations.**—For the purposes of this Code, the term "minor alterations" shall mean minor changes or modifications in a building or any part thereof, excluding additions thereto, that do not in any way affect health or the fire or structural safety of the building. Minor alterations shall not include any of the work described or referred to in Section C26-104.3, or any other work for which a permit is required under the provisions of Section SUB–ARTICLES 109.0 through 116.0.

§C26-104.2 **Ordinary repairs.**—For the purposes of this Code, the term "ordinary repairs" shall mean replacements or renewals of existing work in a building, or of parts of the service equipment therein, with the same or equivalent materials or equipment parts, that are made in the ordinary course of maintenance and that do not in any way affect health or the fire or structural safety of the building or the safe use and operation of the service equipment therein. Ordinary repairs shall not include any of the work described or referred to in Section C26-104.3, or any other work for which a permit is required under the provisions of SUB-ARTICLES 109.0 through 116.0.

§C26-104.3 **Work not constituting minor alterations or ordinary repairs.**—For the purposes of this Code, minor alterations or ordinary repairs shall not include the cutting away of any wall, floor, or roof construction, or any portion thereof; or the removal, cutting, or modification of any beams or structural supports; or the removal, change, or closing of any required means of egress; or the rearrangement or relocation of any parts of the building affecting loading or exit requirements, or light, heat, ventilation, or elevator requirements; nor shall minor alterations or ordinary repairs include additions to, alterations of, or rearrangement, relocation or removal of any standpipe or sprinkler piping, water distribution piping, house sewer, private sewer, or drainage system, including leaders, or any soil, waste or vent pipe, or any gas distribution system, or any other work affecting health or the fire or structural safety of the building.

SUB-ARTICLE 105.0 MAINTENANCE

§C26-105.2   **Owner responsibility.**—Responsible at all times for safe maintenance of the building and its facilities.

SUB-ARTICLE 106.0 MATERIALS, ASSEMBLIES, FORMS AND METHODS OF CONSTRUCTION

§C26-106.1   **General requirements.**—Materials.—As per this Code.
§C26-106.2   **Acceptance requirements.**—
   (1) Code test method.—
   (2) Board of Standards and Appeals approval.—All materials legally accepted prior to effective date of this Code shall be permitted.
§C26-106.4   **Alternate or equivalent materials.**—May be permitted by Commissioner.

SUB-ARTICLE 107.0 SERVICE EQUIPMENT

§C26-107.4   **Alternate or equivalent equipment.**—May be permitted by Commissioner.

SUB-ARTICLE 108.0 APPROVAL OF PLANS

§C26-108.3   **Applicant.**—Can file in behalf of owner.
§C26-108.4   **Plans.**—Amount of copies.
§C26-108.5   **Applicant's statement.**—A signed authorization and statement of work plan.

SUB-ARTICLE 109.0 PERMITS

§C26-109.1   **When permits required.**—
§C26-109.2   **Types of permits.**—New Building, Alteration, Demolition, Plumbing, Signs, etc.
§C26-109.4   **Application for permit.**—
§C26-109.5   **Applicant.**—Owner or authorized agent.
§C26-109.9   **Time limitation of application.**—12 months to start, or be renewed.

SUB-ARTICLE 110.0 APPLICATIONS FOR NEW BUILDING PERMITS

§C26-110.2   **Plans required.**—Applications and plans to have all necessary information.

SUB-ARTICLE 114.0 APPLICATIONS FOR PLUMBING PERMITS

§C26-114.1   **General requirements.**—As per requirements of Sections C26-108.0 and C26-109.0: To have name and address of licensed plumber and evidence of having workmen's compensation insurance.

§C26-114.2   **Plans required.**—Plans required for plumbing permits to have single lines and show riser diagram, plumbing layout and summation of plumbing loads, pipe sizes and materials for soil, waste, vent, water supply, gas distribution piping and storm water piping. Summation of plumbing loads to mean the amount of fixture units and square feet of drained area.

(d) For new plumbing systems show.—Sewer data: Elevation of lowest plumbing fixture; number and size of sewer connections; a statement from the Department of Public Works (Sewer Department) for type and size of sewer (Combined, Storm or Sanitary sewer). Location of sewer connections; and the elevation of top of the street sewer. Water supply data: Size and type of material of the water service piping to be installed; also a statement from the Department of Water Supply, Gas and Electricity giving the minimum water pressure in the street water main, and the location of the connection to be made.

§C26-114.3   **Exemptions from plan requirements.**—Temporary installations, and work as stated in Section C26-114.4 for repair slips.

§C26-114.4   **Alteration and repair slip.**—

(a) For work not to exceed $1000.00 in a 12-month period.

(b) Add only one plumbing fixture.

(c) Replace or add plumbing fixtures to existing roughing, or a minor repair.

§C26-114.5   **Exemptions from permit requirement.**—Installation or servicing of gas piping or equipment performed by a Utility Company (Gas Company) under the jurisdiction of the Public Service Commission.

SUB-ARTICLE 118.0 ISSUANCE OF PERMITS

§C26-118.1   **Approval of permit application.**—Permit to be approved or rejected by the Commissioner.

§C26-118.3   **Signature to permit.**—Permit to have signed approval of Commissioner or authorized representative.

§C26-118.5   **Notice of commencement of work.**—At least 24 hours written notice shall be given to the Commissioner before the commencement of any work for which a permit has been issued.

§C26-118.6   **Expiration of permit.**—Permit expired by limitation if not started in 12 months.

§C26-118.7   **Revocation of permit.**—Commissioner may revoke permit if not complied with.

SUB-ARTICLE 119.0 CONDITIONS OF PERMIT

§C26-119.1   **Payment of fees.**—Fees for application to be paid before permit can be issued.

§C26-119.2   **Compliance with Code, etc.**—

§C26-119.3 **Compliance with application, plans, etc.**—Work to comply with application and plan.

§C26-119.5 **Compliance with safety requirements.**—Work to comply with safety requirements of Code and all applicable laws and regulations.

SUB-ARTICLE 120.0 DEPARTMENT INSPECTIONS

§C26-120.1 **Right of entry and inspections.**—

§C26-120.3 **General provisions.**—Required inspections and tests.

§C26-120.5 **Inspections during progress of work.**—Underground, rough, etc.

§C26-120.6 **Final inspection.**—Before issuance of Certificate of Occupancy, etc.

SUB-ARTICLE 121.0 CERTIFICATES OF OCCUPANCY (C.O.)

§C26-121.2 **New buildings.**—

§C26-121.3 **Altered buildings.**—

§C26-121.4 **Existing buildings.**—C.O. can be obtained if after departmental inspections Commissioner is satisfied that no violation exists.

§C26-121.5 **Change of occupancy or use.**—

§C26-121.6 **Temporary Certificate of Occupancy.**—Permission for 90 days temporary occupancy for parts of building that are safe for occupancy. May be renewed for a further time.

SUB-ARTICLE 123.0 STOP-WORK ORDER

§C26-123.1 **Stop-work notice and order.**—Issued by the Commissioner for work being done without a permit, or in an illegal manner.

SUB-ARTICLE 201.0 DEFINITIONS

Words that are *italic* are defined in this section.

ACCESSORY BUILDING.—A *building,* the *use* or occupancy of which is incidental to that of the main *building.*

ACCESSORY USE.—A *use* or *occupancy* incidental to the principal *use* or *occupancy* of a *building.*

ACCESS STAIR.—A stair between two floors, which does not serve as a *required exit.* (See EXTERIOR STAIR and INTERIOR STAIR.)

ADDITION.—An extension or increase in *floor area* or *height* of a *building* that increases its exterior dimensions.

ADJOINING GRADE ELEVATION.—The average elevation of the final *grade* adjoining all exterior *walls* of a *building,* calculated from grade elevations taken at intervals of 10 feet around the perimeter of the *building.*

AIR CONDITIONING.—The process by which the temperature, humidity, movement, cleanliness, and odor of air circulated through a space are controlled simultaneously.

AIR-SUPPORTED STRUCTURE.—A *structure* consisting of skin diaphragms made of flexible material, which achieves its shape, support, and stability from internal air pressure.

ALLOWABLE SOIL PRESSURE.—The maximum stress permitted in soil of a given type and under given conditions.

ALLOWABLE STRESS.—The maximum stress permitted at a given point in a structural member under given conditions.

ALTERATION.—Any *addition,* or change or modification of a *building,* or the *service equipment* thereof, that affects safety or health and that is not classified as a *minor alteration* or *ordinary repair.* The moving of a *building* from one location or position to another *shall* be deemed an alteration.

AMUSEMENT ATTRACTION.—A game of chance or skill, or similar activity, in which the public participates as a form of amusement.

AMUSEMENT DEVICE.—A mechanically operated device or *structure,* open to the public, *used* to convey persons in any direction as a form of amusement.

APARTMENT HOUSE.—(See MULTIPLE DWELLING.)

APPROVED.—When used in connection with plans, *shall* mean approved by the *Commissioner;* when used in connection with materials and equipment, *shall* mean approved by the *Board;* otherwise *shall* mean approved by the Department or Agency indicated by the text.

ARCHITECT.—A *person* licensed to practice the profession of architecture under the Education Law of the State of New York.

AREA OF REFUGE.—A floor area to which egress is made through a *horizontal exit* or *supplemental vertical exit.*

AREAWAY.—A space below *grade,* adjacent to a *building,* open to the outer air and enclosed by walls.

ASSEMBLY SPACE.—Any part of a *place of assembly,* exclusive of a stage, that is occupied by numbers of *persons* during the major period of *occupancy.* Every *tier of seating* shall be considered a separate assembly space.

ATTIC.—The space between the ceiling framing of the topmost *story* and the underside of the *roof* framing.

AUTOMATIC.—As applied to an *opening protective, shall* mean a door, window, damper, or other device, and its assembly, which is normally open and is designed to close automatically when subjected to a predetermined temperature, rate of temperature rise, or abnormal smoke condition.

AUTOMATIC DRY STANDPIPE SYSTEM.—A *standpipe system* in which all piping is filled with air, either compressed or at atmospheric pressure. Water enters the system through a control valve actuated either automatically by the reduction of air pressure within the system or by the manual activation of a remote control located at each hose station.

AUTOMATIC DRY PIPE SPRINKLER SYSTEM.—A *sprinkler system* in which the piping up to the sprinkler heads is filled with air, either compressed or at atmospheric pressure, with the water supply controlled by a Type A or Type B *dry pipe valve.*

AUTOMATIC FIRE PUMP.—A pump that maintains a *required* water pressure in a fire-extinguishing system and which is actuated by a starting device adjusted to cause the pump to operate when the pressure in the system drops below a predetermined pressure, and to stop the pump when the pressure is restored.

AUTOMATIC OPERATION.—As applied to an *elevator, shall* mean operation whereby the starting of the car is effected in response to the momentary actuation of operating devices at the landing, and/or of operating devices in the car identified with the landings, and/or in response to an automatic starting mechanism, and whereby the car is stopped automatically at the landings.

AUTOMATIC WET PIPE SPRINKLER SYSTEM.—A *sprinkler system* in which all piping and sprinkler heads are at all times filled with water under pressure which is immediately discharged when a sprinkler head operates, with the water continuing to flow until the system is shut off.

AUTOMOTIVE LIFT.—A vehicle-lifting device, the purpose of which is to raise an entire vehicle to provide accessibility for under-chassis service.

AUTOMOTIVE REPAIR SHOP.—A *building* or space in which *motor vehicles* are repaired.

AUTOMOTIVE SERVICE STATION.—A *building,* space, or *premises used* for the storage and sale of motor fuels, and which may also have facilities for lubrication, minor repairs, or washing of *motor vehicles.*

BACKFLOW (Water Supply).—The flow of water or other substances into the distribution pipes of a *potable water* supply from any source other than the intended source.

BALLOON FRAME.—Light timber *construction* in which the exterior *walls* consist of studs that are either continuous through floors or interrupted only by thickness of plates.

BASEMENT.—A *story* partly underground, but having less than one-half its clear height (measured from finished floor to finished ceiling) below the *curb level;* except that where the *curb level* has not been legally established, or where every part of the *building* is set back more than 25 ft. from a *street line,* the height *shall* be measured from the *adjoining grade elevation.* (See CELLAR.)

BEARING.—As applied to a wall or *partition, shall* mean supporting any vertical load in addition to its own weight.

BELT-DRIVE MACHINE.—As applied to an *elevator, shall* mean an indirect-drive machine having a single belt or multiple belts as the connecting means.

BOARD.—The Board of Standards and Appeals of the City of New York.

BOARDER (ROOMER, LODGER).—An individual living within a household who pays a consideration for such residence and does not *occupy* such space as an incident of employment therein.

BREEZEWAY.—A *structure* open to the outdoors consisting of a *roof,* roof supports, and floor, connecting a garage or other *accessory building* with a *dwelling.*

BUILDING.—An enclosed *structure* including *service equipment* therein. The term *shall* be construed as if followed by the phrase "*structure, premises,* or part thereof," unless otherwise indicated by the text.

BUILDING HOUSE DRAIN.—That part of the lowest piping of a *drainage system* that receives the discharge from the soil, waste, and other drainage pipes and conveys it to the *building house sewer* by gravity. The building house drain *shall* be considered to extend 5 ft. outside the exterior wall of the *building.*

BUILDING HOUSE DRAIN (COMBINED).—A *building house drain* that conveys storm water in combination with *sewage* or other drainage.

BUILDING HOUSE DRAIN (SANITARY).—A *building house drain* that carries *sewage* only.

BUILDING HOUSE DRAIN (STORM).—That part of the lowest piping of a storm *drainage system* that receives clear water drainage from *leaders,* surface run-off, ground water, subsurface water, condensate, cooling water, or other similar storm or clear drainage and conveys it to the *building house storm sewer* by gravity. The building house storm drain *shall* be considered to extend 5 ft. outside the exterior wall of the *building.*

BUILDING HOUSE SEWER.—That part of the horizontal piping of a drainage system that extends from the end of the *building house drain* and that receives the discharge of the *building house drain* and conveys it to a *public sewer, private sewer,* individual *sewage-disposal system,* or other point of disposal.

BUILDING HOUSE SEWER (COMBINED).—A *building house sewer* that conveys *sewage* in combination with storm water and other clear water wastes.

BUILDING HOUSE SEWER (SANITARY).—A *building house sewer* that carries *sewage* only.

BUILDING HOUSE STORM SEWER.—That part of the horizontal piping of a storm *drainage system* that extends from the *building house storm drain* to the public storm sewer, combined sewer, or other point of disposal.

BUILDING SECTION.—A room, floor, group of floors, wing, or any other portion of a *building* contained within *fire divisions.*

BUILDING SUB-HOUSE DRAIN.—That portion of a house *drainage system* that cannot drain by gravity into the *building house sewer.*

BULKHEAD.—An enclosed *structure* on or above the *roof* of any part of a *building,* enclosing a *shaft,* stairway, tank, or *service equipment,* or other space not designed or *used* for human occupancy. (See PENTHOUSE and ROOF STRUCTURE.)

CAR DOOR OR GATE.—As applied to an *elevator, shall* mean the sliding portion of the car that closes the opening giving access to the car.

CAR DOOR OR GATE SWITCH.—As applied to an *elevator, shall* mean an electrical device, the function of which is to prevent operation of the driving machine by the normal operating device unless the car door or gate is in the closed position.

CAR-SWITCH OPERATION.—Operation of an *elevator* wherein the movement and direction of travel of the car are directly and solely under the control of the operator by means of a manually operated car switch or of continuous-pressure buttons in the car.

CASING-OFF.—The elimination of the frictional forces between a portion of a *pile* and the surrounding soil by use of a sleeve between the *pile* and the soil.

CATCH PLATFORM.—A platform or other *construction* projecting from the face of a *building,* supported therefrom, and *used* to intercept the fall of objects and to protect individuals and property from falling debris.

CELLAR.—A *story* partly underground, but having one-half or more of its clear height (measured from finished floor to finished ceiling) below the *curb level;* except that where the *curb level* has not been legally established, or where every part of the *building* is set back more than 25 ft. from a *street line,* the height shall be measured from the *adjoining grade elevation.* Cellars *shall* not be counted as stories in measuring the *height* of buildings. (See BASEMENT.)

CERTIFICATE OF OCCUPANCY.—(See Section 121.0.)

CHARGING CHUTE (INCINERATOR).—An enclosed vertical passage through which refuse is fed to an incinerator.

CHARGING GATE (INCINERATOR).—A gate in an incinerator *used* to control the flow of combustion gases into the *charging chute* and the entry of refuse into the combustion chamber.

CHIMNEY.—A vertical enclosure containing one or more *flues used* to remove hot gases from burning fuel, refuse, or from industrial processes.

CHIMNEY CONNECTOR.—A pipe or metal breeching that connects combustion equipment to a *chimney.*

CITY.—The City of New York.

CLOSED SHAFT.—A *shaft* enclosed at the top.

COLLECTING SAFE AREA.—A *safe area* that receives occupants from the *assembly space it serves,* as well as from other *safe areas.*

COMMISSIONER.—The Commissioner of Buildings of the City of New York, or his duly authorized representative.

COMPRESSOR (REFRIGERATION).—A machine used for the purpose of compressing a *refrigerant.*

CONCENTRATED LOAD.—A conventionalized representation of an element of *dead* or *live load* whereby the entire load is assumed to act either at a point or within a limited area.

CONCURRENT LOADS.—Two or more elements of *dead* or *live load* that, for purposes of design, are considered to act simultaneously.

CONSTRUCTION.—Any or all work or operations necessary or incidental to the erection, demolition, assembling, installing, or equipping of *buildings,* or any *alterations* and operations incidental thereto. The term "construction" *shall* include land clearing, grading, excavating, and filling. It *shall* also mean the finished product of any such work or operations.

CONSTRUCTION CLASS (GROUP).—The category in which a *building* or space is classified by the provisions of Article 3, based on the *fire-resistance ratings* of its *construction* elements.

CONSOLE LIFT.—A section of the *floor area* of a theater or auditorium that can be raised or lowered.

CONTRACTOR.—A *person* undertaking *construction.*

CONTROLLED INSPECTION.—(See Section C26-106.3.)

COATINGS, FIRE-RETARDANT.—A material applied to the surface of a building material to improve its *flame spread rating.*

CORRIDOR.—An enclosed public passage providing a means of access from rooms or spaces to an *exit.* (See EXIT PASSAGEWAY.)

COURT.—An *inner court* or *outer court.*

CROSS AISLE.—An aisle in a *place of assembly* usually parallel to rows of seats connecting other aisles or an aisle and an *exit.*

CROSS-CONNECTION (FIRE EXTINGUISHING SYSTEM).—Piping between risers and *Siamese connections* in a *standpipe* or *sprinkler system.*

CROSS-CONNECTION (POTABLE WATER SYSTEM).—A physical connection or arrangement between two otherwise separate piping systems, one of which contains *potable water,* and the other of which contains water of questionable safety, or steam, gases, or chemicals whereby there can be a flow from one system to another.

CURB LEVEL.—The legally established level on the curb in *front* of a *building,* measured at the center of such *front.* When a *building* faces on more than one *street,* curb level *shall* mean the average of the legally established levels of the curbs at the center of each *front.*

CURB LINE.—The line coincident with the face of the *street* curb adjacent to the roadway.

DATUM.—(See Section 110.3.)

DEAD END (EXIT).—A portion of a *corridor* in which the travel to an *exit* is in one direction only.

DEAD LOAD.—Materials, equipment, *constructions,* or other elements of weight supported in, on, or by the *building* (including its own weight) that are intended to remain permanently in place.

DECIBEL.—A unit of measurement of the loudness of sound. A division of a logarithmic scale for expressing the ratio of two amounts of power or energy. The number of decibels denoting such a ratio is 10 times the logarithm of the ratio.

DELUGE SPRINKLER SYSTEM.—An open head *sprinkler system* without water in the system piping, with the water supply controlled by an automatic valve operated by smoke or heat-responsive devices installed throughout the sprinklered area, and independent of the sprinkler heads.

DEMOLITION.—The dismantling or razing of all or part of a *building,* including all operations incidental thereto.

DEPARTMENT.—The Department of Buildings of the City of New York.

DRAINAGE SYSTEM.—All the piping within public or private *premises,* which conveys *sewage,* rainwater, or other liquid wastes to a legal point of disposal, but shall not include the mains of public sewer system or private or public sewage-treatment or disposal plant.

DRAFT CURTAIN.—A *noncombustible* curtain suspended in a vertical position from a ceiling for the purpose of retarding the lateral movement of heated air, gases, and smoke along the ceiling in the event of fire.

DRAFT HOOD.—A device placed in and made part of a *chimney, vent connector,* or combustion equipment, to (1) insure the ready escape of the products of combustion in the event of no draft, back-draft, or stoppage beyond the draft hood, (2) prevent a back-draft from entering the equipment, or (3) neutralize the effect of excessive stack action of the *chimney flue* upon the operation of the equipment.

DRY PIPE VALVE.—A valve that automatically controls the water supply to a *sprinkler system* so that the system beyond the valve is normally maintained dry.

DUCT (VENTILATION).—A pipe, tube, conduit, or an enclosed space within a wall or *structure,* used for conveying air.

DUMBWAITER.—A hoisting and lowering mechanism equipped with a car that moves in guides in a substantially vertical direction, the floor area of which does not exceed 9 sq. ft., whose total inside height, whether or not provided with fixed or movable shelves, does not exceed 4 ft., the capacity of which does not exceed 500 lbs., and that is used exclusively for carrying materials.

DWELLING.—Any *building occupied* in whole or in part as the temporary or permanent home or residence of one or more *families.*

DWELLING UNIT.—One or more rooms in a *dwelling* or *building* that are arranged, designed, *used* or intended for *use* by one or more *families.*

ELECTRICALLY SUPERVISED.—As applied to a control circuit, *shall* mean that in the event of interruption of the current supply or in the event of a break in the circuit, a specific signal will be given.

ELEVATOR.—A hoisting and lowering mechanism equipped with a car or platform that moves in guides in a substantially vertical direction, and that serves two or more floors of a *building.*

EMERGENCY INTERLOCK RELEASE SWITCH.—As applied to an *elevator, shall* mean a device to make inoperative, in case of emergency, door or gate electric contacts or door interlocks.

ENGINEER.—A *person* licensed to practice the profession of engineering under the Education Law of the State of New York.

EQUIVALENT UNIFORM LOAD.—A conventionalized representation of an element of *dead* or *live load,* used for the purposes of design in lieu of the actual *dead* or *live load.*

ESCALATOR.—A power-driven, inclined, continuous stairway used for raising or lowering passengers.

EXIT.—A means of egress from the interior of a *building* to an *open exterior space* which is provided by the use of the following, either singly or in combination: exterior door openings, enclosed *vertical exits, exit passageways, horizontal exits, interior stairs, exterior stairs,* or fire escapes; but not including access stairs, aisles, corridor doors, or *corridors.*

EXIT PASSAGEWAY.—A horizontal extension of a *vertical exit,* or a passage leading from a *yard* or *court* to an *open exterior space.*

EXTERIOR SEPARATION.—The shortest distance across an unobstructed outdoor space measured from the furthest projection of the exterior wall of a *building* to an *interior lot line* or to a line halfway between the wall and that of any other *building* on the same lot, or to the centerline of an adjacent *street* or other *public space.*

EXTERIOR STAIR.—A stair open to the outdoor air, that serves as a *required exit.* (See ACCESS STAIR and INTERIOR STAIR.)

FACING.—As applied to a *sign, shall* mean the surface of the *sign,* upon, against, or through which the message of the *sign* is exhibited.

FAMILY.—A single *person,* or two or more *persons* related by blood or marriage, and living together and maintaining a common household, with not more than four *boarders, roomers,* or *lodgers;* or a group of not more than four *persons,* not necessarily related by blood or marriage, and maintaining a common household.

FIRE ALARM.—A system, automatic or manual, arranged to give a signal indicating a fire emergency.

FIRE AREA.—A *floor* area enclosed by *fire divisions* and/or exterior walls.

FIRE CANOPY.—A solid horizontal projection, extending beyond the exterior face of a *building* wall, located over a wall opening so as to retard the spread of fire through openings from one *story* to another.

FIRE DISTRICTS.—The geographical territories established under Article 4 for the regulation of *occupancy groups* and *construction classes* within such districts.

FIRE DIVISION.—Any construction, vertical, horizontal or otherwise, having the *required fire-resistance rating* and structural stability under fire conditions to provide a fire barrier between adjoining *buildings* or between adjoining or superimposed *fire areas* or *building sections* within the same *building.*

FIRE DOOR.—An *opening protective* in the form of a door and its assembly.

FIRE-PROTECTION RATING.—The time in hours, or fractions thereof, that an *opening protective* and its assembly will withstand fire exposure as determined by a fire test made in conformity with specified standards of Article 5.

FIRE-RESISTANCE RATING.—The time in hours, or fractions thereof, that materials or their assemblies will withstand fire exposure as determined by a fire test made in conformity with a specified standard of Article 5.

FIRE RETARDANT TREATED WOOD.—Wood that has been pressure impregnated with chemicals so as to reduce its combustibility.

FIRE SECTION.—A sprinklered area within a *building* that is separated from other areas by *noncombustible* construction having at least a 2-hour *fire-resistance rating.*

FIRE SEPARATION.—Any construction, vertical, horizontal, or otherwise, having the *required fire-resistance rating* to provide a fire barrier between adjoining rooms or spaces within a *building, building section,* or *fire area.*

FIRESTOP.—A solid or compact, tight closure to retard the spread of flames or hot gases within concealed spaces.

FIRE WALL.—A *fire division* in the form of a wall.

FIRE WINDOW.—An *opening protective* in the form of a window and its assembly.

FLAME SPREAD RATING.—The measurement of the comparative rate of propagation of flame over the surface of a material as determined by a fire test made in accordance with a specified standard in Article 5.

FLAMMABLE.—Capable of being easily ignited when exposed to flame, and which burns intensely, or has a rapid rate of flamespread.

FLASH POINT.—The lowest temperature at which a liquid gives off sufficient vapor to form an ignitable mixture with air near the surface of the liquid or within the vessel used.

FLOOR AREA.—The projected horizontal area enclosed inside of walls, *partitions,* or other enclosing *construction.*

FLOOR AREA (NET).—When used to determine the *occupant load* of a space, *shall* mean the horizontal occupiable area within the space, excluding the thickness of walls, and *partitions,* columns, furred-in spaces, fixed cabinets, equipment, and accessory spaces such as closets, machine and equipment rooms, toilets, stairs, halls, *corridors, elevators* and similar unoccupied spaces.

FLUE.—An enclosed passageway in a *chimney* to carry products of combustion to the outer air.

FOLDED PLATE.—An assembly consisting of one or more units, each unit of which is formed by two or more individually planar elements, termed plates, intersecting at angles.

FOOTING.—A *foundation* element consisting of an enlargement of a *foundation pier* or *foundation wall,* wherein the soil materials along the sides of and underlying the element may be visually inspected prior to and during its construction.

FOUNDATION (BUILDING).—A *construction* that transfers *building* loads to the supporting soil.

FOUNDATION PIER.—A *foundation* element consisting of a column embedded into the soil below the lowest floor to the top of a *footing* or *pile cap.* Where a pier bears directly on the soil without intermediate *footings* or *pile caps,* the entire length of the column below the lowest floor level *shall* be considered as a foundation pier. Foundation piers *shall* be limited to piers so constructed that the entire surface of the sides of the pier and the *bearing* material under the lower end of the pier can be visually inspected prior to or during *construction,* but which will be concealed in the final work. Piers below the lowest floor or *basement* level that will be exposed and open to inspection in the final work *shall* be considered as columns. Types of *construction* wherein the sides cannot be visually inspected *shall* be considered as piling.

FOUNDATION WALL.—A wall extending below *grade.*

FRAMEWORK.—As applied to a *sign, shall* mean the supports, uprights and bracing of the *sign.*

FRESH AIR.—Outdoor air.

FRONT.—As applied to *building* location on a *lot, shall* mean the distance between lines drawn through the most remote points of the *building* perimeter, projected at right angles to a *frontage space.*

FRONTAGE SPACE.—A *street;* or an open space outside of a *building,* not less than 30 ft. in any dimension, that is accessible from a *street* by a driveway, lane, or alley at least 20 ft. in width, and that is permanently maintained free of all obstructions that might interfere with its use by the Fire Department.

FRONT YARD.—A *yard* extending along the full length of a *street line.*

GAS DISTRIBUTION PIPING.—All piping from the house side of the *gas meter piping* that distributes gas supplied by a public utility to all fixtures and apparatus used for illumination or fuel in any *building.*

GAS METER PIPING.—The piping from the shutoff valve inside the building to the outlet of the meter.

GAS SERVICE PIPING.—The supply pipe from the street main through the building wall and including the stopcock or shutoff valve inside the building.

GRADE.—The finished surface of the ground, either paved or unpaved.

GRADE BEAM.—A beam, at, near, or below *grade,* spanning between footings, *pile caps* or *foundation piers,* and supporting walls or other elements of a *building.*

GRANDSTAND.—A *structure used* to support spectators, either standing or seated, usually outdoors.

GROUND SIGN.—A *sign* supported by uprights or braces in or upon the surface of the ground.

HABITABLE ROOM.—A residential room or space, having an area exceeding 59 sq. ft. in which the ordinary functions of domestic life are carried on, and which includes bedrooms, living rooms, studies, recreation rooms, kitchens, dining rooms and other similar spaces, but does not include closets, halls, stairs, laundry rooms, or bathrooms.

HEIGHT (BUILDINGS).—The vertical distance from the *curb level* to the highest point of the *roof beams* in the case of flat roofs, or to a point at the average height of the gable in the case of roofs having a pitch of more than 1 ft. in 4½ ft.; except that where the *curb level* has not been legally established, or where every part of the building is set back more than 25 ft. from a *street line,* the height *shall* be measured from the *adjoining grade elevation.*

HEREAFTER.—On or after the effective date of this Code.

HERETOFORE.—Before the effective date of this Code.

HOISTWAY.—An enclosed or partly enclosed *shaft* used for the travel of an *elevator, dumbwaiter,* platform, or bucket.

HOISTWAY DOOR.—As applied to an *elevator, shall* mean the hinged or sliding portion of a *hoistway* enclosure which closes the opening giving access to a landing.

HOISTWAY DOOR INTERLOCK.—A device used to prevent the operation of the driving machine of an *elevator* by the normal operating device unless the *hoistway door* is locked in the closed position, and also used to prevent the opening of the *hoistway door* from the landing side unless the car is within the landing zone and is either stopped or being stopped.

HORIZONTAL EXIT.—(See Section C26-604.6.)

ILLUMINATED SIGN.—A sign designed or arranged to give forth or reflect light from an attached artificial source.

IMPACT LOAD.—A kinetic load of short duration such as that resulting from moving machinery, *elevators,* craneways, vehicles, etc.

INDEPENDENT POLE SCAFFOLD.—A scaffold supported by multiple rows of uprights, and not depending on the *building* for support.

INDIRECT WASTE PIPE.—A drain pipe used to convey liquid wastes which does not connect directly with the *drainage system,* but which discharges into the house *drainage system* through an air break into a *trap,* fixture, receptacle, or interceptor.

INDUSTRIAL LIFT.—A hoisting and lowering mechanism of a nonportable power-operated type for raising or lowering material vertically, operating entirely within one *story* of a *building.*

INDUSTRIAL WASTE.—Liquid, gaseous, or solid substances, or a combination thereof, resulting from any process of industry, manufacturing, trade or business, or from the development or recovery of any natural resource.

INNER COURT.—Any open area, other than a *yard* or portion thereof, that is unobstructed from its lowest level to the sky and that is bounded by either *building walls,* or *building walls* and one or more *lot lines* other than a *street line* or *building* walls, except for one opening on any open area along an *interior lot line* that has a width of less than 30 ft. at any point.

INTERIOR LOT LINE.—A *lot line* other than a *street line.*

INTERIOR STAIR.—A stair within a *building,* that serves as a *required exit.* (See ACCESS STAIR and EXTERIOR STAIR.)

LAGGING (PILE).—Pieces of timber or other material attached to the sides of *piles* to increase resistance to penetration through soil.

LAMELLA.—*Shell construction* in which the *shell* is formed by a lattice of interlacing members.

LANDING DOOR.—(See HOISTWAY DOOR.)

LEADER.—A vertical drainage pipe for conveying storm water from *roof* or gutter drains to a *building house storm drain, building house drain (combined),* or other means of disposal. The leader *shall* include the horizontal pipe to a single *roof* drain or gutter drain.

LESSEE.—The *person* in possession of a *building* under a lease from the owner thereof.

LICENSE.—A *written* document issued by the *Commissioner* authorizing a *person* to perform specific acts in, or in connection with, the *construction* or *alteration* of *buildings,* or the installation, *alteration,* and *use* and operation of *service equipment* therein.

LIVE LOAD.—All occupants, materials, equipment, *constructions* or other elements of weight supported in, on, or by a *building* that will or are likely to be moved or relocated during the expected life of the *building.*

LOAD-BEARING.—(See BEARING.)

LOADING RAMP.—A hinged, mechanically operated lifting device *used* for spanning gaps and/or adjusting heights between loading surfaces, or between loading surfaces and carriers.

LODGER.—(See BOARDER.)

LOT.—A portion or parcel of land considered as a unit. A zoning lot.

LOT LINE.—A line dividing one land unit from another, or from a *street* or other *public space.* A boundary line of a zoning *lot.*

MANUAL FIRE PUMP.—A pump that feeds water into a fire-extinguishing system that must be started by either the building personnel or members of the Fire Department.

MARQUEE SIGN.—A *sign* placed flat against the front or side fascia of a marquee.

MECHANICAL VENTILATION.—The process of introducing outdoor air into, or removing vitiated air from a *building* by mechanical means. A mechanical ventilating system may include air-heating, air-cooling, or *air-conditioning* components.

MECHANIZED PARKING GARAGE EQUIPMENT.—Special devices in mechanical parking garages that operate in either stationary or horizontal moving hoistways, that are exclusively for the conveying of automobiles, and in which no *persons* are normally stationed on any level other than the receiving level and in which each automobile during the parking process is moved by means of a power-driven transfer device, on and off the elevator, directly into parking spaces or cubicles.

MEZZANINE.—An intermediate floor between the floor and ceiling of any space. When the total gross *floor area* of all mezzanines occurring in any story exceeds 33-1/3% of the gross *floor area* of that *story,* such mezzanine shall be considered as a separate story.

MINOR ALTERATIONS.—(See Section C26-104.0.)

MORTAR (GROUT).—A mixture of cementitious materials, fine aggregates and water.

MOTOR VEHICLE.—A conveyance propelled by an internal combustion engine and having a fuel storage tank capacity of more than 2 gals.

MOVING WALK.—A passenger-carrying device on which *persons* stand or walk, and in which the passenger-carrying surface remains parallel to its direction of motion and is uninterrupted.

MULTIPLE DWELLING.—A building containing three or more *dwelling units.* Multiple dwelling shall not be deemed to include a hospital, school, convent, monastery, asylum, or other public institution.

NONAUTOMATIC SPRINKLER SYSTEM.—A *sprinkler system* in which all pipes and sprinkler heads are maintained dry and which is supplied with water through a Fire Department *Siamese connection.*

NONAUTOMATIC STANDPIPE SYSTEM.—A *standpipe system* in which all piping is maintained dry, and which is supplied with water through a Fire Department *Siamese connection.*

NONBEARING.—As applied to a wall or *partition, shall* mean one that supports no vertical load other than its own weight.

NONCOMBUSTIBLE.—A material which, in the form in which it is used in *construction,* will not ignite and burn when subjected to fire. However, any material which liberates *flammable gas* when heated to any temperature up to 1380°F for 5 minutes shall not be considered noncombustible. No material shall be considered noncombustible which is subject to increase in combustibility beyond the limits established above, through the effects of age, fabrication, or erection techniques, moisture, or other interior or exterior atmospheric conditions.

NONCONCURRENT LOADS.—Two or more elements of *dead* or *live load* which, for purposes of design, are considered not to act simultaneously.

NONLOAD-BEARING.—(See NONBEARING.)

OCCUPANCY.—The purpose or activity for which a *building* or space is *used* or is designed or intended to be *used.*

OCCUPANCY GROUP.—The category in which a *building* or space is classified by the provisions of Article 3, based on its *occupancy* or *use.*

OCCUPANT LOAD.—The number of occupants of a space, floor or *building* for whom *exit* facilities *shall* be provided.

OCCUPIABLE ROOM.—A room or space, other than a *habitable room,* designed for human *occupancy* or *use,* in which *persons* may remain for a period of time for rest, amusement, treatment, education, dining, shopping, or other similar purposes, or in which occupants are engaged at work.

OCTAVE.—The interval between two sounds having a basic frequency ratio of two. By extension, the octave is the interval between any two frequencies having the ratio 2:1. The standard octave bands are:

FREQUENCY (CPS)

Mid-Frequency	63	125	250	500	1000	2000	4000	8000
Approximate Lower Frequency	45	90	180	355	710	1400	2800	5600
Limits Upper	90	180	355	710	1400	2800	5600	11200

OIL BUFFER.—As applied to an *elevator, shall* mean a buffer using oil as a medium which absorbs and dissipates the kinetic energy of a descending car or counterweight.

OPEN EXTERIOR SPACE.—A *street* or other *public space;* or a *yard, court,* or plaza open on one or more sides and unroofed or open on all sides, which provides egress to a *street* or *public space.*

OPEN PARKING LOT.—A *lot,* or portion thereof, *used* for the storage or sale of more than four *motor vehicles,* but not *used* for the repair or servicing of such vehicles.

OPEN PARKING STRUCTURE.—A structure open to the outdoors 50% or more on two or more sides of each *story, used* for the parking of *motor vehicles.*

OPEN SHAFT.—A *shaft* open to the outdoor air at the top.

OPENING PROTECTIVE.—An assembly of materials and accessories, including frames and hardware installed in an opening in a wall, *partition,* floor, ceiling, or *roof* to prevent, resist, or retard the passage of flame, smoke, or hot gases.

ORDINARY REPAIRS.—(See Section C26-104.0.)

OUTER COURT.—Any open area, other than a *yard* or portion thereof, that is unobstructed from its lowest level to the sky and that, except for an outer court opening upon a *street line,* a *front yard,* or a *rear yard,* is bounded by either *building* walls or *chimney walls* and one or more *lot lines* other than a *street line.*

OUTRIGGER SCAFFOLD.—A scaffold, the platform of which is built upon supports cantilevering beyond the walls of the *building.*

OWNER.—A *person* having legal title to *premises;* a mortgagee or vendee in possession; a trustee in bankruptcy; a receiver or any other *person* having legal ownership or control of *premises.*

PARAPET.—The continuation of an exterior wall, *fire* wall, or *party* wall above the *roof* line.

PARKING TIER.—A general level of parking.

PARTITION.—A vertical unit or assembly of materials that separates one space from another within any *story* of a *building.*

PARTY WALL.—A *fire division* on an *interior lot line* common to two adjoining *buildings.*

PENTHOUSE.—An enclosed *structure* on or above the *roof* of any part of a *building,* which is designed or *used* for human occupancy. (See BULKHEAD and ROOF STRUCTURE.)

PERMIT.—A *written* document issued by the *Commissioner* authorizing the *construction* or *alteration* or *demolition* of a *building,* or the installation, *alteration,* or *use* and operation of *service equipment* therein.

PERSON.—An individual, partnership, corporation, or other legal entity.

PILE.—A structural element introduced into the ground to transmit loads to lower strata and of such construction that the material underlying the base of the unit or along the sides cannot be visually inspected.

PILE CAR.—A *construction* encasing the heads of one or more piles which transfers loads to the *pile* or *piles.*

PLACE OF ASSEMBLY.—An enclosed room or space in which 75 or more *persons* gather for religious, recreational, educational, political, or social purposes, or for the consumption of food or drink, or for similar group activities, but excluding such spaces in *dwelling units;* or an outdoor space in which 200 or more *persons* gather for any of the above reasons.

PLASTIC.—A material that contains as an essential ingredient an organic substance of large molecular weight, is solid in its finished state and, at some stage in its manufacture or its processing into finished articles, can be shaped by flow.

PLASTIC, SLOW BURNING.—A *plastic* having a rate of combustion within the limits of a specified standard of Article 5.

PLATFORM FRAME.—Light timber *construction* in which the exterior walls and *bearing* walls consist of studs which are interrupted at floors by the entire thickness of the floor *construction.*

PLUMBING.—The practice, materials, and fixtures used in the installation, maintenance, extension, and *alteration* of all piping, fixtures, appliances, equipment, and appurtenances in connection with any of the following: sanitary drainage or storm drainage facilities, the venting system and the public or private water supply systems, within or adjacent to any *building;* also the practice and materials used in the installation, maintenance, extension, or *alteration* of storm water, liquid-waste, or sewerage, and water-supply systems of any *premises* and their connection with any point of public disposal or other acceptable terminal.

PLUMBING FIXTURES.—Installed receptacles, devices, or appliances that are supplied with water or which receive or discharge liquids or liquid-borne wastes.

PLUMBING SYSTEM.—The water-supply and distribution pipes; *plumbing fixtures* and traps; soil, waste, and vent pipes; *building house drains* and *building house sewers* including their respective connections, devices, and appurtenances within the property lines of the *premises;* and water-treating or water-using equipment.

POLE FOOTING.—A type of *construction* in which a pole embedded in the ground, and extending upward to form a column, is used for both column and *footing.*

PONDING.—The collection of rainwater.

POTABLE WATER.—Water free from impurities present in amounts sufficient to cause disease or harmful physiological effects. Its bacteriological and chemical quality shall conform to the requirements of the Department of Health.

POWER-OPERATED SCAFFOLD.—Any form of scaffold that is propelled vertically by the use of power machinery.

PREMISES.—Land, improvements thereon, or any part thereof.

PRIVATE GARAGE.—A *building* or enclosed space *used* for the parking or storage of not more than four *motor vehicles* having fuel storage tanks of 26 gals. capacity or less, and in which no repair, body work, or painting of vehicles is conducted, and in which no gasoline, oil, or similar products are dispensed.

PRIVATE SEWER.—A sewer privately owned and controlled by public authority only to the extent provided by law.

PROJECTING SIGN.—A *sign* affixed to an exterior wall of a building and extending more than 15 in. beyond the wall surface.

PUBLIC GARAGE.—A *building* or space used for the parking or storage of *motor vehicles*, other than an *automotive service station, automotive repair shop, open parking structure,* or *private garage.* Truck loading and shipping areas shall be classified as public garages.

PUBLIC SEWER.—A sewer entirely controlled by public authority.

PUBLIC SPACE.—An open space outside of a *building*, which is dedicated or devoted to public use by lawful mapping or by any other lawful procedure.

PURE TONE.—A sound wave of a single frequency, so called to distinguish it from a complex tone.

REAR LOT LINE.—Any *lot line,* except a *street line,* that is parallel or within 45° of being parallel to, and does not intersect any *street line* bounding such *lot.*

REAR YARD.—A *yard* extending for the full length of a *rear lot line.*

REBOUND.—Recovery of displacement due to release or reduction of applied load.

REFRIGERATION.—The process by which heat is absorbed from a substance by expansion or vaporization of a refrigerant.

REQUIRED.—*Shall* mean required by the provisions of this Code.

RETAINING WALL.—A wall designed to prevent the lateral displacement of soil or other materials.

RIGGING LOFT.—A space above a stage, designed and used for the flying and storage of *scenery and scenic elements.* A space used for the occasional flying of incidental props during a performance shall not be deemed to constitute a rigging loft.

ROOF.—The topmost slab or deck of a *building,* either flat or sloping, with its supporting members, not including vertical supports.

ROOF COVERING.—The covering applied to the exterior surface of a *roof* for weather resistance, fire resistance, wear, and/or appearance, but not including insulation.

ROOF SIGN.—A *sign* erected and maintained on or above the *roof* of a *building.*

ROOF STRUCTURE.—An unenclosed *structure* on or above the *roof* of any part of a *building*. (See BULKHEAD and PENTHOUSE.)

ROOMER.—(See BOARDER.)

SAFE AREA.—Any interior or exterior space that serves as a means of egress by providing a transitional area from, and that also serves as a normal means of entry to, *an assembly space.*

SAFETY (CAR OR COUNTERWEIGHT).—A mechanical device attached to an *elevator* car frame or to an auxiliary frame, or to the counterweight frame, to stop and hold the car or counterweight in case of predetermined overspeed or free fall, or if the hoisting ropes slacken.

SCENERY AND SCENIC ELEMENTS.—Any or all of those devices ordinarily used on a stage in the presentation of a theatrical performance, such as back drops, side tabs, teasers, borders or scrim, rigid flats, set pieces, and all properties, but not including costumes.

SCHOOL.—An elementary school, high school, or college, either public or private.

SEATING SECTION.—An area of seating bounded on all sides by aisles, *cross aisles,* walls, or *partitions.*

SELF-CLOSING.—As applied to an *opening protective shall* mean a door, window, damper, or other device, and its assembly, that is normally kept in a closed position and that is equipped with an *approved* device to insure immediate closing after having been opened for use.

SELF-RELIEVING CONSTRUCTION.—*Construction* using a type of framing in which the connections are capable of developing a known and dependable moment capacity but which, under larger moments, are capable of rotating (without fracture) an amount sufficient to accommodate the deflection due to the excess of the applied moment over the moment capacity.

SERVICE EQUIPMENT.—Equipment, including all components thereof, which provides sanitation, power, light, heat, cooling, ventilation, air-conditioning, refuse disposal, fire-fighting, transportation, or similar facility for a building which by design becomes a part of the *building,* and which is regulated by the provisions of this Code.

SEWAGE.—Any liquid waste containing animal or vegetable matter in suspension or solution, and may include liquids containing chemicals in solution.

SEWAGE DISPOSAL SYSTEM.—A system for the disposal of *sewage* by means of a septic tank, cesspool, or mechanical treatment, all designed for use apart from a *public sewer* to serve a single establishment, *building,* or development.

SEWAGE EJECTOR.—A mechanical device used to pump or eject *sewage.*

SHAFT.—A vertical, inclined, or offset passage, or *hoistway,* penetrating through two or more floors of a *building* or through a floor and *roof.* (See CLOSED SHAFT and OPEN SHAFT.)

SHALL.—As used in this Code, is always to be construed as mandatory.

SHELL.—A *structure* consisting of a curved or folded slab whose thickness is small compared to its other dimensions, and which is characterized by its three-dimensional load-carrying behavior. The term *shall* include those forms of *construction* that approximate slab surfaces, such as *lamellas* and lattices.

SIAMESE CONNECTION.—A fitting connected to a fire-extinguishing system and installed on the outside of a *building,* with two hose inlets for use of the Fire Department, to furnish or supplement the water supply to the system.

SIDE LOT LINE.—Any *lot line* that is not a *street line* or a *rear lot line.*

SIDEWALK ELEVATOR.—A freight *elevator* that operates between a sidewalk or other area outside of a *building* and floor levels inside the *building* below such area, which has no landing opening into the *building* at its upper limit of travel, and which is not used to carry automobiles.

SIDE YARD.—A *yard extending* along a *side lot line* from the *required front yard* (or from the *street line* if no *front yard* is *required*) to the *required rear yard* (or to the *rear lot line* if no *rear yard* is *required*).

SIDEWALK SHED.—A *construction* over a public sidewalk, *used* to protect pedestrians from falling objects.

SIGN.—An outdoor *structure,* banner, or other device, designed or *used* as an advertisement, or announcement for the information or attraction of the public; consisting of the *framework* and all letters, words, numerals, illustrations, illumination, decorations, trademarks, emblems, symbols, or other figures or characters.

SINGLE POLE SCAFFOLD.—A platform resting on putlogs or crossbeams, the outer ends of which are supported on ledgers secured to a single row of posts or uprights, and the inner ends of which are supported by a wall.

SMOKE-STOP DOOR.—A door or set of doors placed in a *corridor* to restrict the spread of smoke and to retard the spread of fire by reducing draft.

SOIL VENT.—(See STACK VENT.)

SOUND POWER.—The rate at which sound energy is radiated by a source.

SOUND POWER LEVEL.—The ratio, expressed in *decibels,* of the *sound power* of a source to the reference power of 10^{-12} watts.

SOUND PRESSURE LEVEL.—The square ratio, expressed in decibels, of a sound pressure to a reference pressure of 0.0002 dynes per square centimeter.

SPANDREL WALL.—That portion of an exterior wall between the top of one opening and the bottom of another in the *story* directly above.

SPARK ARRESTER.—A device to prevent sparks, embers, or other ignited material above a given size from being expelled to the atmosphere from the top of a *chimney.*

SPECIAL WASTE.—Wastes that require special treatment before entry into the normal *plumbing system.*

SPRAY BOOTH.—A compartment in which spraying with any substance is carried on, consisting of at least two sides, a back, and a top.

SPRAYING SPACE OR DIPPING SPACE.—Any portion of a *building* in which the actual work of spraying, dipping, or immersing any article with or into *flammable* substances takes place.

SPRINKLER ALARM.—An apparatus constructed and installed so that a flow of water through the sprinkler system, equal to or greater than that required for a single automatic sprinkler head, will cause an alarm to be given.

SPRINKLER SYSTEM.—A system of piping and sprinkler heads connected to one or more sources of water supply.

STACK.—(See CHIMNEY.) Also, a general term applying to any vertical line of soil, waste, vent, or inside leader piping. It shall not include vertical fixture and vent branches that do not extend through the *roof* or that pass through not more than two *stories* before being reconnected to the *vent stack* or *stack vent.*

STACK VENT.—The extension of a soil or waste stack above the highest horizontal drain connected to a plumbing *stack.*

STAGE LIFT.—A movable section of a stage floor, designed to carry scenery between staging areas and the stage, and also *used* to be raised to and temporarily retained at elevations above or below the stage level.

STANDPIPE SYSTEM.—A system of piping, for fire-fighting purposes, consisting of connections to one or more sources of water supply, and serving one or more hose outlets.

STORM DRAIN.—(See BUILDING STORM DRAIN.)

STORM SEWER.—A sewer used for conveying rainwater, surface water, condensate, cooling water, or similar clear liquid wastes which do not contain organic materials or compounds subject to decomposition.

STORY.—That portion of a *building* that is between a floor level and the next higher floor level or *roof* above.

STREET.—A thoroughfare dedicated or devoted to public use by legal mapping or other lawful means.

STREET FLOOR.—A floor, usually the principal entrance floor, that is not more than ½ *story* above or below *grade* at the location from which egress is provided to the *street.*

STREET LINE.—A *lot line* separating a *street* from other land.

STREET MAIN.—(See WATER MAIN and GAS SERVICE PIPING.)

STRUCTURE.—An assembly of materials forming a *construction* for *occupancy* or *use,* including among others: *buildings,* stadia, tents, reviewing stands, platforms, stagings, observation towers, radio towers, tanks, trestles, open sheds, coal pockets, shelters, fences, and display *signs.*

SUBSTRATE.—A surface upon which a finish material is directly applied and which extends completely behind such finish material.

SUMP PIT.—A tank or pit that receives clear liquid wastes that do not contain organic materials or compounds subject to decomposition, located below the normal grade of the gravity system and that must be emptied by mechanical means.

SUMP PUMP.—A mechanical device used to pump the liquid waste from a *sump pit* into the gravity *drainage system.*

SUPPLEMENTAL VERTICAL EXIT.—An enclosed stair, ramp, or *escalator* providing means of egress to an area of refuge at another level nearer to the *street floor.*

TIER OF SEATING.—A general level of seating, such as an orchestra (usually the main tier), a balcony, or gallery.

TRAILER CAMP.—A *lot* or parcel of land used for temporary or permanent *occupancy* by two or more mobile homes or travel trailers.

TRANSFER COLUMN.—A column supported by beams, girders, trusses, or similar members and reacting on two or more columns at a lower level.

UNIFORMLY DISTRIBUTED LOAD.—A conventionalized representation of an element of *dead* or *live load,* as a load of uniform intensity, distributed over an area.

USE (USED).—The purpose for which a *building, structure,* or space is *occupied* or utilized, unless otherwise indicated by the text. Use (used) *shall* be construed as if followed by the words "or as intended, arranged, or designed to be used."

VAULT (SIDEWALK).—Any space below the surface of the sidewalk portion of a *street,* that is covered over, except those openings that are used exclusively as places for descending, by means of steps, to the *cellar* or *basement* of any *building.*

VENT (GAS).—A *flue* or *duct,* used to convey the products of combustion from gas-fired equipment to the outdoor air by natural draft.

VENT STACK (PLUMBING).—A vertical vent pipe extending through more than two *stories,* which is then connected to a *stack vent* or is otherwise extended through the *roof,* installed primarily for the purpose of providing circulation of air to and from any part of a *drainage system.*

VENT SYSTEM (COMBUSTION).—A gas *vent* or *chimney,* together with a *vent connector* that forms a continuous unobstructed passageway from gas-burning equipment to the outdoor air for the purpose of removing *vent* gases.

VENT SYSTEM (PLUMBING).—A pipe or pipes installed to provide a flow of air to or from a *drainage system* or to provide a circulation of air within such system to protect *trap seals* from siphonage and back pressure.

VERTICAL EXIT.—A stair, ramp, or *escalator* serving as an *exit* from one or more floors above or below the *street floor.*

WALL SIGN.—A *sign* affixed to the exterior wall of a *building,* no part of which projects more than 15 in. from the wall surface.

WATER-DISTRIBUTION PIPING.—The pipes in a *building* or *premises* that convey water from the *water service pipe* to the *plumbing fixtures* and other water outlets.

WATER (STREET) MAIN.—A water-supply pipe for public or community use controlled by public authority.

WATER-SERVICE PIPE.—The pipe from the *water (street) main* or other source of water supply to the *building* served.

WATER SUPPLY SYSTEM.—The *water-service pipe,* the *water-distribution piping,* and all of the necessary connecting pipes, fittings, control valves, and appurtenances used for conveying water in a *plumbing system.*

WET STANDPIPE SYSTEM.—A *standpipe system* in which all of the piping is filled with water under pressure, that is immediately discharged upon the opening of any hose valve.

WINDING-DRUM MACHINE.—As applied to an *elevator, shall* mean a geared-drive machine in which the hoisting ropes are fastened to, and wind on, a drum.

WORKMEN'S HOIST.—A hoisting and lowering mechanism equipped with a car that moves in guides in a substantially vertical direction and that is used primarily for raising and lowering workmen to the working levels.

WRITING (WRITTEN).—The term *shall* be construed to include handwriting, typewriting, printing, photo-offset, or any other form of reproduction in legible symbols or characters.

WRITTEN NOTICE.—A notification in *writing* delivered by hand to the *person* or parties intended, or delivered at, or sent by mail, to the last business address known to the party giving such notice.

YARD.—That portion of a *lot* extending open and unobstructed from the lowest level to the sky along the entire length of a *lot line.*

ZONE.—A vertical division of a *building* fire *standpipe system* used to establish the water working pressures within the system and also to limit the pressure at the lowest hose outlet in the zone.

ZONING RESOLUTION.—The Zoning Resolution of the City of New York, effective December 15, 1961, including all amendments thereto.

SUB-ARTICLE 202.0 ABBREVIATIONS

bhp: brake horsepower	gpm: gallons per minute
Btu: British thermal unit	gps: gallons per second
C: Centigrade	sec.: second
cfm: cubic feet per minute	swp: steam working pressure
cps: cycles per second	sq. ft.: square foot
cu. ft.: cubic feet	sq. in.: square inch
db: decibel	hp: horsepower
dia.: diameter	hr.: hour
F: Fahrenheit	in.: inch
fpm: feet per minute	INR: impact noise rating
fps: feet per second	I.P.S.: iron pipe size
fsp: fire standpipe	lb.: pound
ft.: foot	mph: miles per hour
gal.: gallon	oz.: ounce

P.C.E.: pyrometric cone equivalent　　psig: pounds per square inch gauge
pcf: pounds per cubic foot　　rpm: revolutions per minute
plf: pounds per linear foot　　sq. yd.: square yard
psf: pounds per square foot　　STC: sound transmission class
psi: pounds per square inch　　Tag: tagliabue
psia: pounds per square inch absolute　　wwp: water working pressure

Note–For abbreviation of name of referenced national organizations see Reference Standard RS 2-1

ARTICLE 3

OCCUPANCY AND CONSTRUCTION CLASSIFICATIONS

TABLE OF CONTENTS

*"§C26-" omitted from Section numbers in this table.

*"§ C26-" omitted from Section numbers in this table.

SUB-ARTICLE OR
   SECTION*
316.0   Mixed Construction
316.1   Classification
316.2   Restrictions

*"§C26-" omitted from Section numbers in this table.

SUB-ARTICLE 303.0   OCCUPANCY GROUP

Table 3-2 gives the letters and numbers of TYPICAL OCCUPANCIES mentioned in various parts of this book. Reference can therefore be made to this table to find the designation of the Type of Occupancy of a building.

IMPORTANT.   Typical example in using Occupancy Classifications Table 3-2:

OCCUPANCY GROUP	DESIGNATION	OCCUPANCY
Residential	J-3	1- and 2-fam. dwelling

§C26-303.2   **Occupancy group B-1.—**

Table 3-2. Typical Occupancies For Occupancy Classifications*

Occupancy Group	Desig- nation	Representative Occupancies
HIGH HAZARD	A	Paint shop and storerooms; industrial smoke houses; grain elevators; tanneries with enameling or japanning; distilleries; sugar, starch, cereal, feed, flour, and grist mills
STORAGE	B-1	Warehouses, storerooms; freight depots; stables; coal; pockets; Group 1 public garages (Group 1)**
	B-2	Warehouses; storerooms; private garages; greenhouses; Group 2 public garages (Group 2)**

*This list of occupancies is representative only and is not complete. See Reference Standard RS 3-3 in City of N. Y. Building Code, Page 210, for additional listings.
  **See SUB-ARTICLE 709.0.

Table 3-2 (Continued). Typical Occupancies For Occupancy Classifications

Occupancy Group	Designation	Representative Occupancies
MERCANTILE	C	Retail stores; shops; sales rooms; markets
INDUSTRIAL	D-1	Baking plants; breweries; automotive repair shops; foundries; heliports; scenery shops
	D-2	Mechanical and electrical equipment rooms; commercial laundries; vocational training shops; laboratories; boiler and furnace rooms; nonresidential kitchens; power plants
BUSINESS	E	Office buildings; banks; civic administration buildings; radio and television stations; telephone exchanges; barber and beauty shops; automotive service stations
ASSEMBLY	F-1a	Theaters; playhouses; opera houses
	F-1b	Churches; lecture halls; courtrooms; convention halls; concert halls; sports arenas; planetariums; motion picture theaters
	F-2	Grandstands; bleachers; stadiums; drive-in theaters; amusement attractions and devices; bandstands; skating rinks
	F-3	Exhibition halls; galleries; gymnasiums; museums; passenger terminals; bowling alleys; billiard parlors; skating rinks
	F-4	Restaurants; nightclubs; cabarets; dance halls; ballrooms; banquet rooms; cafeterias; snack bars; taverns; coffee houses
EDUCATIONAL	G	Schools; academies; universities; libraries
INSTITUTIONAL	H-1	Jails; prisons; reformatories; mental institutions
	H-2	Hospitals; sanitariums; clinics; nursing homes; orphanages; homes for the aged; day nurseries
RESIDENTIAL	J-1	Hotels; motels; lodging houses; rooming houses
	J-2	Apartment houses; apartment hotels; school dormitory buildings
	J-3	One-family and two-family dwellings; rectories; convents
MISCELLANEOUS	K	Sheds; fences; signs

§C26-700.0 to §C26-718.8   **IMPORTANT** Different types of occupancies such as: dry-cleaning establishments, public garages, swimming pools, spray booths. Occupancies with radio-active materials, etc., requirements stated with each type of occupancy. Types of equipment permitted. For full details see Building Code.

ARTICLE 7

SPECIAL USES AND OCCUPANCIES

TABLE OF CONTENTS

*" §C26-" omitted from Section numbers in this table.

*"§C26-" omitted from Section numbers in this table.

*"§C26-" omitted from Section numbers in this table.

SUB-ARTICLE 704.0 BOILER AND FURNACE ROOMS

§C26-704.2   **Enclosure.**–Enclosed boilers and furnace rooms. All types of buildings except one- and two-family dwellings.
High-pressure boiler rules.
Louvre ventilation.–Minimum 144 sq. in.

SUB-ARTICLE 714.0 SWIMMING POOLS

§C26-714.2   **Construction.**–For specific details see Building Code.

§C26-714.3   **Dressing facilities.**–Toilet and shower facilities required.

§C26-714.5   **Water circulation, water treatment, and drainage.**–Per ARTICLE 16 and the Health Code.

SUB-ARTICLE 1207.0   VENTILATION OF SPECIAL SPACES

§C26-1207.3   **Bathrooms and toilet rooms.**—

(a) By natural means.—At least 5% of floor area, minimum 1½ sq. ft. except H-1 and H-2 OCCUPANCY.

(b) By individual vent shaft.—One sq. ft. plus 1/3 additional sq. ft. for each additional water closet or urinal above 2 in number.

(c) By mechanical ventilation.—For one water closet or urinal, minimum 50 cu. ft. per minute. For more than one water closet or urinal, minimum 40 cu. ft. per minute per water closet or urinal.

ARTICLE 14

HEATING AND COMBUSTION EQUIPMENT

TABLE OF CONTENTS

*" §C26-" omitted from Section numbers in this table.

*"§C26-" omitted from Section numbers in this table.

*"C26-" omitted from Section numbers in this table.

SUB-ARTICLE 1401.0 INSPECTIONS AND TESTS FOR EQUIPMENT USE PERMITS

§C26-1401.1   **Boilers.**—Boilers with more than 350,000 Btu input to be inspected by an Inspector of the Building Department Boiler Division.

SUB-ARTICLE 1402.0 LICENSES AND CERTIFICATES

§C26-1402.1   **High-pressure boiler operating engineer license.**—See preceding Section B26-4.1.

§C26-1402.2   **Oil burner equipment installer license.**—See preceding Section B26-8.4.

§C26-1402.3   **Certificates.**—Non-automatic burner or preheating device.—Requires a Certificate of Fitness issued by the Fire Commissioner, for the "operator" or "person in charge" of its operation.

(Flash point for fuel oil, 100 degrees F or over, permitted.)

ARTICLE 15

CHIMNEYS AND GAS VENTS

TABLE OF CONTENTS

*"§C26-" omitted from Section numbers in this table.

*"§C26-" omitted from Section numbers in this table.

ARTICLE 15

CHIMNEYS AND GAS VENTS

TABLE OF CONTENTS

§C26-1500.0 to §C26-1505.4

SUB-ARTICLE 1501.0 CHIMNEYS

SUB-ARTICLE 1504.0 GAS VENT SYSTEMS

For full details see Building Code.

ARTICLE 16

PLUMBING AND GAS PIPING

TABLE OF CONTENTS

*"§C26-" omitted from Section numbers in this table.

*" §C26-" omitted from Section numbers in this table.

SUB-ARTICLE 1600.0 GENERAL

§C26-1600.1   **Scope.**—Minimum requirements for plumbing: (also see Section C26-104.3 and Section P100.0). Design, Installation, Alteration, Repair (replacement), and Relocation of (1) Water supply; (2) Fixtures; (3) Waste and vent; (4) Storm water only when Storm Sewer or Combined Sewer in street, or if Storm water piping is in building; (5) Gas piping.

To be performed by or under direct supervision of a Licensed Plumber.

EXCEPTION.—Gas piping and gas equipment at the street side of gas meter to be done by a utility company (Gas Company) under the jurisdiction of the Public Service Commission.

§C26-1600.2   **Standards.**—The provisions of Reference Standard RS-16 shall be part of this article.

§C26-1600.3   **Definitions.**—For definitions to be used in the interpretation of this article, see ARTICLE 2.

§C26-1600.4   **Plans.**—For the requirements governing the filing of plans and the work to be shown on plans, see ARTICLE 1.

§C26-1600.5   **Permits.**—For the requirements governing application for building permits, see ARTICLE 1.

§C26-1600.6   **General requirements.**—Plumbing and gas piping shall be designed and installed so as to satisfy the following conditions and the requirements of Reference Standard RS-16.

(a) Every structure with human occupancy to have a potable water supply.—

(1) No connection with unsafe water (as well water).

(2) No cross-connection with any drainage system.

(b) Sufficient volume of water required.—Supply to keep plumbing fixtures sanitary, and without undue noise (no water hammer, etc.).

(c) Water conservation.—No water waste.

(d) Safeguarding against explosion.—Pressure relief valves supplied where necessary.

(e) Connections to public water and sewer systems.—

(1) If public water main in street, connection to building required.

(2) If public sewer in street, connection to building required.

For AMENDED RULING regarding Section C26-1600.6 (e)(2) for "Availability of Public Sewers," see DEPARTMENT OF BUILDINGS Directive Number 24 – 1970. (See Appendix, page 190.)

(f) Well water systems.—Requires approval of Commissioner; Department of Health; Department of Water Supply, Gas and Electricity; and Department of Public Works.

(g) Drainage system design and maintenance.—Drainage systems to be properly designed and to have necessary cleanouts.

(h) Exclusion of certain substances from the plumbing system.—

(1) Illegal types of sewage, as rubbish, oil, gasoline, etc., cannot be deposited into building drainage or sewer system.

(2) Industrial wastes.—If, in the opinion of the Department of Buildings or Department of Public Works, the wastes are detrimental to the public sewer system or to public health, sewage must be treated before being discharged into the public sewer. When "plans" are filed for this type of work, waste substance other than that from the human body must be stated.

(i) Prevention of contamination of food, etc.—(Indirect waste required.)

(j) Drainage below street level.—(Use sewage ejector or sump.)

(k) Disposal of storm water.—Provision to be made to connect to storm sewer or combined sewer when available. If no sewer available use method approved by Commissioner, as.—Dry wells or splash-pans, if ground is of clay, etc.

(l) Required plumbing fixtures.—All dwellings in occupancy groups J-2 and J-3 to have a water closet, basin, bathtub or shower, and sink.

(m) Smooth-surfaces required.—Plumbing fixtures to be of smooth, non-absorbent material and free from fouling surfaces.

(n) Location of plumbing fixtures.—

(o) Liquid-seal traps and vents required.—

(p) Exhausting of foul air to outside.—

(q) Materials and workmanship.—To be free from defects. (New material shall be used, with possible exceptions.)

(r) Condemned equipment.—Defective material prohibited.

(s) Prevention of sewer flooding.—(Use approved backwater valve.)

(t) Test of plumbing system.—(Water, smoke, peppermint.)

(u) Proper maintenance.—

(v) Protection of ground and surface water.—Disposal of sewage in approved manner, as per approval of Commissioner, Department of Health, and Department of Public Works.

(w) Weather Protection.—Water service piping: minimum, 4 ft. below exterior grade; house sewer: minimum, 3 ft. below exterior grade; and piping in exterior parts of building to be protected from frost.

(x) Structural safety.—Parts of plumbing system not to obstruct structural safety.

(y) Strains and stresses in pipes.—Pipes to be protected from strain (use swing and expansion joints).

(z) Installation limitations.—No piping permitted in elevator shafts, etc.

§C26-1600.7   **Use of nonconforming material or equipment**.—Materials and equipment to comply with rules of Building Code. See Reference Standard RS-16.

§C26-1600.8   **Fire protection for pipes**.—Where pipes pass through construction required to have a fire-resistance rating, they shall comply with the requirements of Section C26-504.5.

§C26-1600.9   **Establishing gas supply**.—It shall be unlawful for any utility company to supply gas to a building, place, or premises in which new meters other than replacement, are required, until a certificate of approval of gas installation from the Department of Buildings is filed with such utility company.

SUB-ARTICLE 1601.0   WATER SUPPLY SYSTEMS

§C26-1601.1   **Public water supply**.—

(a) Where City Water Main available.—Every building to be connected.

(b) If insufficient pressure available to reach upper floors, power pumps required.

§C26-1601.2   **Private water supply.**—Subject to approval of Commissioner.

§C26-1601.3   **Cross-connection of supplies and identification.**—No cross-connection of City Water Supply to any other water supply, or to the drainage system, permitted.

SUB-ARTICLE 1602.0   DRAINAGE SYSTEMS

§C26-1602.1   **Permits.**—

(a) Permit for house sewers or disposal system shall be obtained from the Department of Public Works.

(b) Permit for sidewalk or street opening shall be obtained from the Department of Highways.

§C26-1602.2   **Individual sewage systems.**—When no sewer in street, install as per orders of Commissioner. When sewer becomes available, connection to be made within one year.

§C26-1602.3   **Construction.**—Drainage systems to be installed as per Reference Standard RS-16.

SUB-ARTICLE 1603.0   HOSPITAL AND INSTITUTIONAL PLUMBING

§C26-1603.1   **Requirements.**—To be installed as per rules of the Building Code and specific modifications of Reference Standard RS-16.

SUB-ARTICLE 1604.0   SWIMMING POOLS

To be installed as per rules of the Building Department. (See SUB-ARTICLE 714.0 and Reference Standard RS-16.)

To be installed as per rules of the Health Department Code.

SUB-ARTICLE 1605.0   EXISTING BUILDINGS AND INSTALLATIONS

§C26-1605.1   **General.**—

Adding two or more fixtures.—All added new work to comply to this Code.

§C26-1605.2   **Existing soil and vent stacks.**—

(a) Location of windows.—When a new building is erected next to an existing building, windows of new building must be over 10 ft. away from any vent stack of old building, unless expenses of raising or relocating stack on old building are agreed upon by owners of old building and expenses paid by owner of new building. Or, vent can be raised not less than 3 ft. above topmost opening.

(b) When the existing adjoining building is higher than the new building, all new soil, waste, or vent stacks of the new building shall be located at least 10 ft. from the common lot line, or shall be carried to a level above the higher existing roof, adequately supported and with the consent of the owners of both the new and existing structures.

SUB-ARTICLE 1606.0 INSPECTION AND TESTS

§C26-1606.1   **Inspection.**—Work to be inspected as to compliance.

§C26-1606.2   **Notification.**—Minimum of 2 days written notice required.

§C26-1606.3   **Testing of plumbing and gas piping systems.**—

(a) Test for breaks or defects.

(b) In presence of Commissioner or Plumbing Inspector of the Department.

(c) Work to be visible for inspection.

(d) Work to comply or be retested.

§C26-1606.4   **Requirements.**—

(a) Drainage and vent systems.—

(1) Roughing.—Test for at least 15 minutes prior to start of inspection.

(a) Water test.—All parts of drainage system to be tested with not less than 10 ft. head of water. System can be tested in sections if all pipes have been submitted to a 10 ft. head of water, except the top 10 ft. of the system.

(b) Air test.—Subject to permission from Commissioner. Minimum of 5 psi to be held without introducing additional air for a period of 15 minutes.

(2) Finished plumbing.—

(a) Smoke test.—

After all fixtures are set, fill traps with water.
Fill drainage system with smoke from a smoke machine.
Seal all openings at roof terminals, after smoke appears.
Maintain pressure of one inch column of water, until completion of inspection.

(b) Peppermint test.—Introduce 2 ounces of oil of peppermint into each stack. Follow by 10 quarts of hot water, minimum of 160 degrees F.

(b) House sewer.—Water test with not less than 10 ft. head of water for minimum of 15 minutes.

(c) Water systems.—Tested to a minimum of 25 per cent above working pressure.

(d) Gas piping systems.—Tested to a minimum of 50 per cent above working pressure. Also tested to a minimum of 6-in. column of mercury, or 3 psi for a minimum of 10 minutes.

(e) Other systems.—Tested as per Reference Standard RS-16.

ARTICLE 17

FIRE ALARM, DETECTION AND EXTINGUISHING EQUIPMENT

TABLE OF CONTENTS

*"§C26-" omitted from Section numbers in this table.

*"§C26-" omitted from Section numbers in this table.

BUILDING CODE REFERENCE STANDARDS
APPENDIX TO TITLE C, PART II

TABLE OF CONTENTS

RS 12   Light, Heat, Ventilation and Noise Control
RS 13   Mechanical Ventilation, Air Conditioning and Refrigeration Systems
RS 14   Heating and Combustion Equipment
RS 15   Chimneys and Gas Vents
RS 16   Plumbing, Drainage and Gas Piping
RS 17   Fire Alarms, Detection and Extinguishing Equipment
RS 18   Elevators and Conveyors
RS 19   Safety of Public and Property During Construction Operations

REFERENCE STANDARD RS-2
DEFINITIONS

REFERENCE STANDARD RS 2-1

Abbreviations of Names of National Organizations

AASHO   American Association of State Highway Officials
AC   American Concrete Institute
AGMA   American Gear Manufacturers Association
AISC   American Institute of Steel Construction, Inc.
AIA   American Insurance Association
AISI   American Iron and Steel Institute
ANSI   American National Standards Institute (Formerly USASI)
APA   American Plywood Association
AREA   American Railway Engineering Association
ASTM   American Society for Testing and Materials
ASCE   American Society of Civil Engineers
ASHRAE   American Society of Heating, Refrigerating and Air Conditioning
         Engineers
ASME   American Society of Mechanical Engineers
AWWA   American Water Works Association
AWS   American Welding Society
AWPA   American Wood Preservers Association
C.S.   Commercial Standard, U.S. Department of Commerce
FHA   Federal Housing Administration, U.S.
F.S.   Federal Specification, U.S.
IBI   Insulation Board Institute
IOS   International Organization for Standardization
MHMA   Mobile Homes Manufacturing Association
NBFU   American Insurance Association (National Board of Fire Under-
         writers)
NFPA   National Fire Protection Association
NFPA   National Forest Products Association (National Lumber Manufactur-
         ers Association)
SJI   Steel Joist Institute
U.L.   Underwriters Laboratories, Inc.
USASI   United States of America Standards Institute (See ANSI)

REFERENCE STANDARD RS-16
PLUMBING AND GAS PIPING

LIST OF REFERENCED NATIONAL STANDARDS

USASI	A21.4	Cement Mortar Lining for Cast Iron Pipe and Fittings	1964
USASI	A21.6	Cast Iron Pipe Centrifugally Cast in Metal Molds for Water or other Liquids	1962
USASI	A21.8	Cast Iron Pipe Centrifugally Cast in Sand-Lined Molds for Water or other Liquids.	1962
USASI	A40.4	Air Gaps in Plumbing Systems	1942
USASI	A40.5	Threaded Cast Iron Pipe for Drainage, Vent, and Waste Services	1943
USASI	A40.6	Backflow Preventers in Plumbing Systems	1943
USASI	A106.1	Standard and Extra Strength Perforated Clay Pipe, Specifications for.	1962
USASI	A106.3	Standard Strength Clay Sewer Pipe, Specifications for	1965
USASI	B2.1	Pipe Threads (Except Dryseal) (Partial Revision of B2.1-1945)	1960
USASI	B16.3	Malleable—Iron Screwed Fittings, 150 and 300 lb. (Revision and Consolidation of B16.3-1951 and B16.19-1951)	1963
USASI	B16.4	Cast-Iron Screwed Fittings, 125 and 250 lb.	1963
USASI	B16.12	Cast-Iron Screwed Drainage Fittings	1965
USASI	B16.15	Cast Bronze Screwed Fittings, 125 and 250 lb. (Revision and Consolidation of B16.15-1958 and B16.17-1949)	1964
USASI	B16.18	Cast Bronze Solder-Joint Pressure Fittings	1963
USASI	B16.22	Wrought Copper and Bronze Solder-Joint Pressure Fittings	1963
USASI	B16.23	Cast-Bronze Solder Joint Drainage Fittings.	1960
USASI	B16.24	Bronze Flanges and Flange Fittings 150 and 300 lb.	1962
USASI	B36.1	Welded and Seamless Steel Pipe, Specifications for.	1966
USASI	B36.2	Welded Wrought-Iron Pipe, Specifications for.	1966
USASI	B36.19	Stainless Steel Pipe	1965
USASI	B36.20	Black and Hot Dipped Zinc-Coated (Galvanized) Welded and Seamless Steel Pipe for Ordinary Uses, Specifications for	1966
USASI	C72.1	Household Automatic Electric Storage-Type Water Heaters, Standard for.	1949
USASI	G8.	Zinc Coated (Galvanized) Iron or Steel Sheets, Coils, etc.	1964

USASI	H23.1	Seamless Copper Water Tube, Specifications for...	1967
USASI	H23.3	Seamless Copper Tube, Specifications for........	1965
USASI	H26.1	Seamless Copper Pipe, Standard Sizes, Specifications for................................	1963
USASI	H26.2	Threadless Copper Pipe, Specifications for.......	1963
USASI	H27.1	Seamless Red Brass Pipe, Standard Sizes, Specifications for................................	1963
USASI	H36.1	Seamless Brass Tube, Specifications for	1967
USASI	Z4.2	Drinking Fountains, Specifications for	1942
USASI	Z21.10.1	Automatic Storage Type Water Heaters with Input Less Than 50,000 Btu Per Hour, Approval Requirements for, Vol. 1	1966
USASI	Z21.22	Relief Valves and Automatic Gas Shut-Off Devices for Hot Water Systems, Listing Requirements for..................................	1964
USASI	Z21.30	Installation of Gas Appliances and Gas Piping	1964
ASME		Boiler Code..............................	1967
ASTM	B32	Specifications for Solder Metal (Tentative).......	1966T
ASTM	B36	Specifications for Brass Plate, Sheet, Strip, and Rolled Bar.............................	1966
ASTM	B121	Specifications for Leaded Brass Plate, Sheet, Strip, and Rolled Bar.........................	1966
ASTM	B135	Seamless Brass Tube, Specifications for	1966
ASTM	B146	Leaded Yellow Brass Sand Casting for General Purposes, Specifications for................	1952
ASTM	B152	Copper Sheet, Strip, Plate, and Rolled Bar, Specifications for............................	1960
ASTM	B260	Brazing Filler Metal (Tentative), Specifications for .	1962T
ASTM	C4	Specifications for Clay Drain Tile..............	1962
ASTM	C13	Specifications for Standard Strength Clay Sewer Pipe (Tentative).........................	1964T
ASTM	C14	Specifications for Concrete Sewer, Storm Drain, and Culvert Pipe	1967
ASTM	C76	Specifications for Reinforced Concrete Culvert, Storm Drain, and Sewer Pipe (Tentative).......	1965T
ASTM	C200	Specifications for Extra Strength Clay Pipe (Tentative).................................	1965T
ASTM	C425	Specifications for Vitrified Clay Pipe Joints Using Materials Having Resilient Properties..........	1966T
ASTM	C428	Specifications for Asbestos-Cement Nonpressure Sewer Pipe (Tentative)....................	1967T
ASTM	C443	Specifications for Joints for Circular Concrete Sewer and Gaskets............................	1965

ASTM C508	Specifications for Asbestos Cement Perforated Underdrain Pipe (Tentative)...................	1967T
ASTM E-84	Method of Test for Surface Burning Characteristics of Building Materials......................	1961
CS 20	Vitreous China Plumbing Fixtures.............	1963
CS 77	Enameled Cast-Iron Plumbing Fixtures.........	1956
CS 111	Earthenware (Vitreous-Glazed) Plumbing Fixtures.	1943
CS 115	Porcelain-Enameled Tanks (Land Use)..........	1960
CS 177	Bituminous-Coated Septic Tanks..............	1962
CS 188	Cast-Iron Soil Pipe and Fittings..............	1966
CS 243	Stainless Steel Plumbing Fixtures.............	1962
CS 270	Non-metallic Pipe and Fittings Acrylonitrile-Butadiene-Styrene (ABS)......................	1965
CS272	Non-metallic Pipe and Fittings Polyvinyl Chloride (PVC)..................................	1965
AWWA C204	Protective Coating Coal-Tar Enamel...........	1951
FS HH-C-536a	Compound; Plumbing-Fixture-Setting..........	1954
FS HH-G-116	Gaskets; Plumbing-Fixture-Setting.............	1936
FS QQ-L-156(1)	Lead Caulking............................	1946
FS QQ-C-40	Caulking; Lead Wool and Lead Pig.............	1965
FS QQ-L-201d	Lead Sheet..............................	1961
FS RR-S-726(1)	Stills, Water, Portable (Without Heating Device), for U.S.P. "Distilled Water".................	1950
FS SS-P-361b	Pipe, Clay, Sewer........................	1962
FS SS-S-169	Sealer, Joint, Sewer, Mineral-Filled, Hot-Pour....	1954
FS WW-F-406a(1)	Flange-Dimensions, Standard: (Classes 125 and 250 Cast-Iron Flanges; Classes 150, 250, and 300 Bronze Flanges) (For Land Use).............	1943
FS WW-H-171C	Hangers and Supports, Pipe.................	1964
FS WW-H-191a	Heater, Water, Steam-Hot Water Heated (Instantaneous, Steam, Water Converter Type).........	1964
FS WW-N-351a(1)	Nipples, Pipe, Threaded....................	1960
FS WW-U-531C	Unions, Pipe Steel or Malleable Iron; Thread Connection.............................	1965
FS WW-P-325	Pipe Bends and Traps; Lead (for) Plumbing and Water-Distribution.......................	1944
FS WW-P-356	Pipe, Cast-Iron; Drainage, Vent, and Waste (Threaded).............................	1936
FS WW-P-360a	Pipe, Cast-Iron; Pressure Gas and Water.........	1959
FS WW-P-401C	Pipe and Pipe Fittings, Cast-Iron, Soil..........	1963
FS WW-P-406b(1)	Pipe Steel (Seamless and Welded) (for Ordinary Use)..................................	1964

REFERENCE STANDARD RS-16

PLUMBING

TABLE OF CONTENTS

Section P100.0 to P116.2

LIST OF TABLES

LIST OF ILLUSTRATIONS

SECTION P100.0 DEFINITIONS

Air break.–(Drainage system).–See Diagram 1

Air chamber.–See Diagram in Rules of the Department of Water Supply, Gas and Electricity in appendix.

Air gap.–(Water distribution system).–See Diagram 1.

Branch.–Piping to fixtures on two, or less, consecutive floors. See Diagram 2.

Building house drain and house sewer.–Lowest piping of drainage system, that extends 5 ft. outside of front wall. See Diagram 3.

    Sanitary.–Carrying sewage only.

    Combined.–Carrying sewage and storm water.

    Storm.–Carrying storm water only.

Building house sewer.–Extends from house drain to point of disposal, sewer, etc. See Diagram 3.

Common, dual, or unit vent.–For 2 fixtures back to back. See diagram 14 and Fig. RS 16-4.

Cross-connection.–Between potable water and questionable supply of water, gas or chemical.

Dead end.–A plugged up drainage pipe 2 ft. or over. See Diagram 4.

Developed length.–Measurement along center line of pipe and fittings. See Diagram 5.

Diameter.–Pipe for waste water in a building drainage system. See Diagram 6.

Drainage system.–All wastes from "Sanitary" system. Also all storm water if there is a "Combined Sewer" or "Storm Sewer" in street. Also if an <u>inside leader</u> installed (when made of galvanized steel or cast iron pipe).

Dry well.–A pit or well for storm water.

Flood level rim.–The top edge of a fixture or tank. See Diagram 1.

Frostproof water closet.–A hopper toilet. No water in toilet bowl. See Diagram 7.

Gas distribution piping.–All gas piping on house side of gas meter.

Gas service piping.–Gas piping from street gas main to gas meter. Under the jurisdiction of a Utility Company (Gas Company).

Indirect waste pipe.–A drain pipe not directly connected to the drainage system. See Diagram 1.

Leader.–A vertical storm water line. See Diagrams 8 and 27.

Local vent.–A ventilating pipe on fixture side of trap, and not connected to the plumbing drainage system. See Diagram 9.

Main.–A system of horizontal or vertical piping other than a branch or stack. See Diagram 10.

Oil Separators.–See P105.4(c) and Fig. RS 16-9 for Definition.

Pitch.–Grade, slope.

pH.–A symbol relating to acidity or alkalinity. 7.0 is considered neutral. Lower values represent acidity and higher values represent alkalinity.

Plumbing.—(See Section C26-1600.1.)
   <u>Installation.</u>—
   <u>Alteration.</u>—
   <u>Repair (Replacement).</u>—
   <u>Relocation.</u>—
Plumbing fixture.—A <u>receptacle</u> which receives and discharges water and other wastes into a drainage system.

Plumbing system.—Water supply system, plumbing fixtures and traps; and the sanitary and storm drainage system on the premises including soil, waste and vent piping.

   (<u>NOT</u> any heating system, apparatus of boiler plant, machine, air-conditioning system or refrigerating system.)

Pool.—Accommodates more than 1 bather at a time. Also a display pool. See Diagram 29.

Potable water.—Pure water.

Relief vent.—For additional circulation of air between drain and vent systems. See Diagram 11.

Riser.—A vertical water supply pipe one full story or more.

Septic tank.—A receptacle between building house trap and a cesspool or leaching field. See Fig. RS 16-12 in Section P113.10.

Sewage ejector.—A mechanical device to dispose of drainage below gravity house drain. See Diagram 24 in Section P108.6.

Sewers.—
   <u>Private.</u>—Privately owned, and controlled by City.
   <u>Public.</u>—City owned, and controlled by City.
   <u>Sanitary.</u>—Receives waste from plumbing fixtures.
   <u>Combined.</u>—Receives sewage and storm water.
   <u>Storm.</u>—Receives rain water or sub-surface water only. See Diagram 12.
Slope.—Grade or pitch.

Soil pipe.—A drainage line that disposes of waste and fecal matter.

Stack.—A vertical soil waste or vent line, for 2 or more floors, or an inside leader line. See Diagram 2.

Sub-house drain.—A drainage system below gravity house drain. See Diagram 24.

Sub-soil drain.—A drain that disposes of sub-surface water. See Diagram 25.

Swimming pool.—A structure for recreational bathing having a depth of 2 ft. or more at any one point. See Diagram 29.

Trap.—A <u>device</u> that prevents passage of air without affecting flow of sewage. See Diagrams 13, 19, and 20.

Trap seal.—The vertical distance between <u>crown weir</u> and <u>dip</u> of trap. See Diagram 13.

Unit vent.—See Diagram 14.

Vacuum breaker.—A device used to prevent backflow by siphonic action.

Vents.—See Diagram 15.

Waste pipe.—Receives discharge from any fixture except a water closet and similar fixture that receives fecal matter, and conveys discharge to house drain, soil or waste pipe.

Water distribution piping.—Conveys water from service piping to plumbing fixtures. See Diagram 16.

Water service piping.—Extends from the city water main to a valve inside the building, or to a point where the supply is fully metered. See Diagram 16.

Yoke vent.—Upward connecting piping to prevent pressure changes in the stacks. See Diagram 17.

LIST OF DIAGRAMS

1. Air Gap
2. Branch and Stack
3. Building House Drain and House Sewer
4. Dead End
5. Developed Length
6. Diameter
7. Frostproof Water Closet
8. Leader
9. Local Vent
10. Main
11. Relief Vent
12. Sewers: Public, Private, Sanitary, Storm
13. Trap
14. Unit Vent, Common Vent, or Dual Vent
15. Vents
16. Water Service Piping and Water Distribution Piping
17. Yoke Vent
18. Wiped Joint
19. Separate Traps for Each Fixture
20. Grease Interceptor
21. Air Chamber
22A. House Supply Tank
22B. Hydropneumatic Pressure Tank (Cylindrical)
23. Fresh Air Inlet
24. Sewage Ejector
25. Sub-soil Drainage
26. Floor Drains
27. Connection of Storm Water Piping to "Combined House Drain"
28. Expansion Joint
29. Swimming Pools

THE FOLLOWING DIAGRAMS GIVE A PICTORIAL DESCRIPTION
OF THE DEFINITIONS ON PRECEDING PAGES

Air Chamber.—See P107.5 and Diagram in Rules of the Department of Water Supply, Gas and Electricity section in appendix at end of the book.

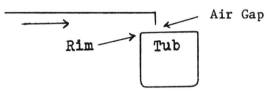

Air Gap.—Diagram 1.

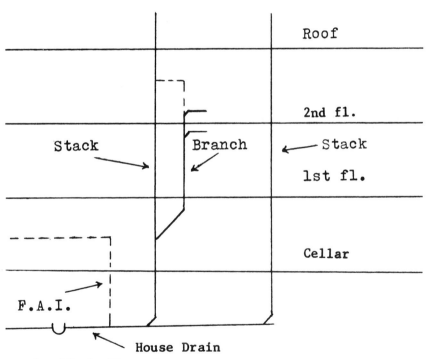

Branch and Stack.—Diagram 2.

Branch Interval.—See Fig. RS 16-7.

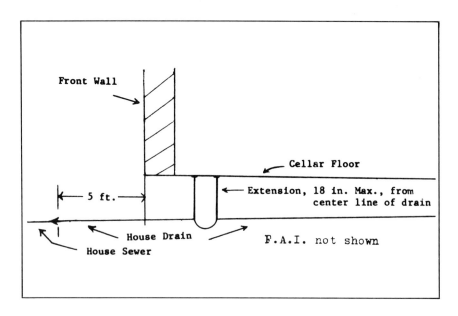

Building House Drain and House Sewer.–Diagram 3. See definitions.

Common Vent, Dual Vent, and Unit Vent.–See Fig. RS 16-4 and Diagram 14.

Continuous Vent.–See Fig. RS 16-4 and Diagrams 19 and 20.

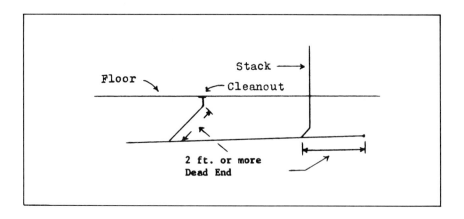

Dead End.–Diagram 4. Permitted to extend cleanout–See P108.8(d).

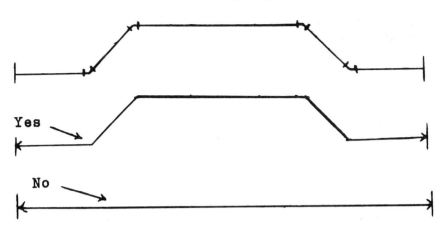

Developed Length.–Diagram 5.

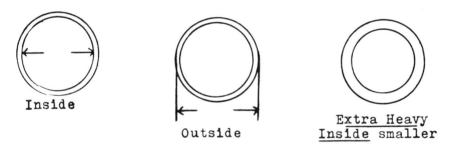

Inside

Outside

Extra Heavy
<u>Inside</u> smaller

Diameter.–Diagram 6.

Expansion Joint.–See P103.1(m), P110.11, and Diagram 28.
Fixture Trap.–See P105.1(a) and Diagrams 13, 19, and 20.
Floor Drain.–See P109.8(d), P104.17, and Diagram 26.
Fresh Air Inlet.–See P108.5 and Diagram 23.

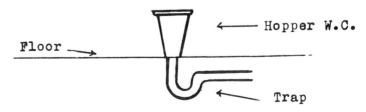

Floor →

← Hopper W.C.

← Trap

Frostproof Water Closet.–Diagram 7.

Interceptor or Grease Trap.–See P105.4(d) and Diagram 20.
Leaching Well or Seepage Pit.–See Fig. RS 16-13.

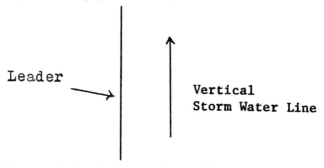

Leader.–Diagram 8. See Definitions, P110.8(c), and Diagram 27 for method for connecting leader line to "Combined House Drain."

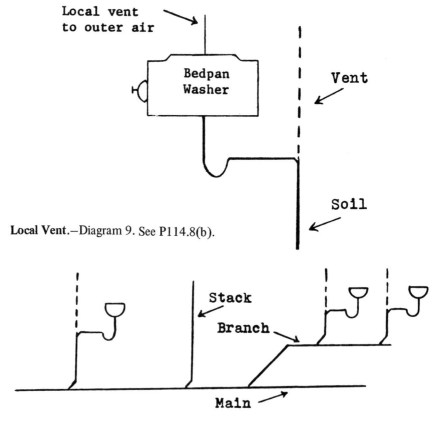

Local Vent.–Diagram 9. See P114.8(b).

Main.–Diagram 10. A system of horizontal or vertical piping other than a branch or stack.

Oil Separators.—See P105.4(c) and Fig. RS 16-9.

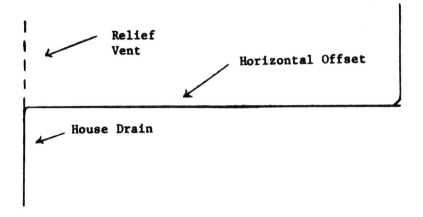

Relief Vent.—Diagram 11. See P109.9 and Fig. RS 16-6.

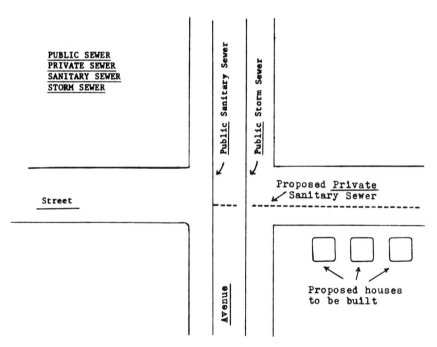

Sewers.—Diagram 12. See Definitions.

Septic Tank.—See Fig. RS 16-12.
Sewage Ejector.—See P108.6 and Diagram 14.
Sub-Soil Drain.—See P108.7 and Diagram 25.
Swimming Pool.—See P116.0 and Diagram 29. (From filter—Indirect connection to drainage system.)

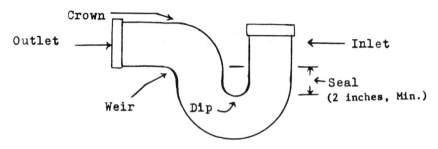

Trap.—Diagram 13.

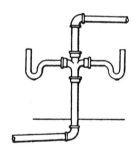

Unit Vent, Common Vent, or Dual Vent.—Diagram 14.

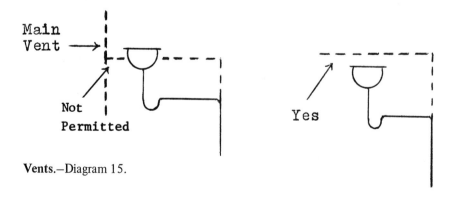

Vents.—Diagram 15.

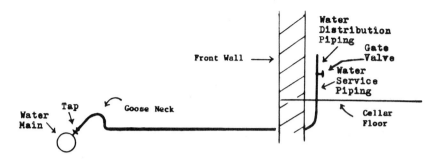

Water Service Piping and Water Distribution Piping.—Diagram 16. Under the jurisdiction of the Department of Water Supply, Gas and Electricity (for) Service Piping.

Wiped Joint.—See P103.1(v) and Diagram 18.

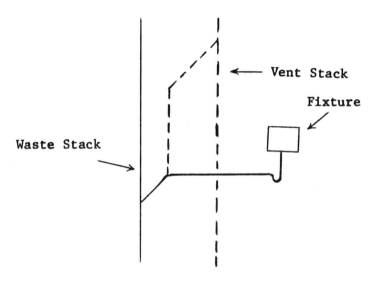

Yoke Vent.—Diagram 17.

SECTION P101.0 GENERAL PROVISIONS

§P101.1   **Protection of pipes.**—

(a) Breakage.—Use sleeves for pipes through wall or floor.

(b) Corrosion.—Under concrete or corrosive material use asphaltum. Tar paper can also be added.

§P101.2   Trenching, excavation and backfill.—

(a) Material for backfill.—Underground piping to be installed on a firm bed.

(b) Trenching methods.—

(1) On poor soil, piping to be properly supported.

(2) Acceptable driving and tunneling methods may be used if open trench is impractical.

(3) Permits for sidewalk and street openings to be obtained from the Department of Highways.

§P101.5   Toilet facilities for workmen.—Requirements as per Table RS 16-5.

SECTION P102.0   MATERIALS

§P102.1   General requirements.—

(a) Materials required.—As per this standard.

§P102.2   Standards for plumbing materials.—

(a) Materials.—**As per Table RS 16-1** or material approved by BS&A.

(b) Plastic material.—Approved type, as per BS&A, may be used in buildings up to 3 stories in height.

The BS&A Supplemental Ruling of June 10, 1970 regarding SECTION P102.2(b) Plastic material

(See DEPARTMENT OF BUILDINGS DEPARTMENTAL MEMO-RANDUM of July 10, 1970 and the CONTENTS of the BS&A ruling in reference to plastic pipe and fittings.):—

1. Authority and Scope

Pursuant to the authority vested in the Board of Standards and Appeals of the City of New York by virtue of Section 666 Paragraph 2 of the Charter of the City of New York and Section P102.2.b of Reference Standard 16 of the Building Code of the City of New York, the Board does promulgate and set forth the following rules for the design, construction and installation of plastic pipe and fittings within the City of New York.

These rules are to be considered as supplemental to and not in substitution of all applicable provisions of the Building Code.

2. Definitions

Where provisions of these Rules differ from provisions of the Building Code, the more restrictive requirements shall apply.

(PVC) Polyvinyl Chloride—
(ABS) Acrylonitrile-Butadiene-Styrene
(CS) Commercial Standards of the United States Department of Commerce National Bureau of Standards—
(ASTM) American Society For Testing And Materials.

3. Application

3.1—The use of plastic pipe and fittings for plumbing systems shall be limited to drain, waste and vent lines in buildings of three (3) stories or less in height as set forth under Sections P102.2.b, P102.4.b.1, P102.4.c.1 of RS16 of the Building Code of the City of New York.

3.2—Connections between fixtures, traps and drain of waste lines shall be by metal pipe and metal fittings only.

4. Physical and Chemical requirements of material

4.1—The physical and chemical properties of all pipe and fittings shall comply with the requirements of Commercial

Standards CS272-65 of the United States Department of Commerce National Bureau of Standards for Polyvinyl Chloride (PVC) pipe and fittings, and of CS270-65 for Acrylonitrile-Butadiene-Styrene (ABS) pipe and fittings and shall be approved by the Board.

5. Tests

5.1—Applicants for approval of PVC or ABS pipe or fittings shall submit certified test reports from an independent testing laboratory satisfactory to the Board, which reports shall show that the material has been tested as follows:

5.2—Pipe and fittings shall be tested in accordance with the test procedures as set forth in CS272-65 for PVC pipe and fittings or in CS270-65 for ABS pipe and fittings.

5.3—PVC pipe and fittings shall be tested in accordance with the requirements of ASTM D635-68 to determine that the pipe and fittings are self-extinguishing.

5.4—ABS pipe and fittings shall be tested in accordance with the requirements of ASTM D635-68 to determine that the pipe and fittings are slow-burning.

6. Marking

6.1—All pipe shall be marked on two sides, 180 degrees apart, in letters not less than 3/16 inches high, in contrasting color, and shall consist of the manufacturer's name or trade mark, nominal pipe size, the symbol PVC or ABS, the type designation (I or II) Schedule 40 CS272-65 for PVC, or CS270-65 for ABS and the symbol of the NATIONAL SANITATION FOUNDATION DRAIN WASTE VENT spaced at intervals of not more than two (2) feet.

6.2—Fittings shall be marked on the body or hub on opposite sides. The marking shall consist of the manufacturer's name or trade mark and the symbol PVC or ABS and the type designation (I or II) for PVC and the symbol of the NATIONAL SANITATION FOUNDATION DRAIN WASTE VENT.

6.3—In addition to the markings as required under 6.1 and 6.2, all pipe and fittings shall bear the labeling required under the conditions of approval by the Board and Section P102.2.b of RS16 of the Building Code of the City of New York.

7. Installation

7.1—Installation of pipe and fittings shall be in accordance with Appendix I and II of CS270-65 or CS272-65, with the following exceptions and additions.

7.2—Rule 6.1 of Appendix I—Delete and substitute as follows: Support horizontal piping at intervals of not more than two (2) ft. for pipes, 1½ inches or less in diameter and not more than three (3) ft. for pipes of larger diameter, at ends of branches and at all points of change of direction. Vertical piping shall be supported at each floor and at mid-height between floors, when story-height does not exceed 10 feet, and at intervals of not more than five (5) feet when the story exceeds ten (10) feet in height. All supports shall permit expansion and contraction of the pipe without binding.

7.3—Rule 6.2 of Appendix I—Delete and substitute as follows: Pipe clamps or brackets shall have a bearing width of at least ¾ inches and shall be of metal. All clamps or brackets shall be installed so that they will not compress, distort or cut into the pipe.

7.4—Rule 6.3 of CS270-65 and CS272-65—Delete in its entirety as the use of this pipe is limited to above ground installation.

7.5—Expansion—Provisions shall be made for expansion and contraction on the basis of 1 inch per 10'-0" run of pipe per 150°F. temperature rise.

7.6—Pitch—Horizontal run of pipe shall be installed at uniform alignment and at uniform slope of ¼ inch per 1 foot of run.

8. Protection

8.1—Passing through walls or floors—Where piping passes through walls or floors it shall be encased in metal sleeves securely fastened to the wall or floor construction. Sleeves shall be not less than 18 gauge steel and not more than ½ inch greater in diameter than the outside diameter of the pipe and shall extend not less than 20 inches beyond each side of the wall or floor construction. The space between the sleeve and the piping shall be fire-stopped by packing with noncombustible material.

8.2—Vertical run of pipe—All vertical runs of pipe shall be enclosed with materials having a fire rating with a minimum of one (1) layer of ⅝ inch thick fire-rated gypsum board. If the pipe is adjacent to a noncombustible wall, the wall may be considered as part of the enclosure. Vertical installation shall comply with Section C26-504.5 and C26-504.7 of the Building Code of the City of New York.

8.3—Horizontal run of pipe—all horizontal runs of pipe shall be protected by either:

8.3.1—Enclosing the pipe with a minimum of one (1) layer of ⅝ inch fire-rated gypsum board, or

8.3.2—By a suspended ceiling constructed of either; one (1) layer of ⅝ inch fire-rated gypsum board; or, one (1) layer of ¾ inch fire-rated noncombustible tile; or, any short-span fire resistive ceiling construction as approved by the Board.

8.3.3—Exception—Structures classified as Group II, Class II-E shall be exempt from the requirements of Rule 8.3.

§P102.3   **Identification of materials.—**

§P102.4   **Piping system materials.**

   (a) Water supply systems.—

    (1) Water service pipe.—Red brass, type "K" copper tube, type "TP" threadless copper, cast iron water pipe, galvanized wrought iron, galvanized steel, grade AA lead pipe for pressure up to 70 psi, and grade AAA lead pipe for pressure over 70 psi. Galvanized pipe used underground to be coated.

Table RS16-1. Standards for Plumbing Materials[a]

Materials	USASI	Other
Ferrous Pipe and Fittings—		
Cast iron soil pipe and fittings, extra heavy and service weights	None	CS 188-66
Cast iron water pipe	A21.6-1962	
	A21.8-1962	
Cast iron pipe, drainage, vent and waste	None	FS-WW-P-356-1936
Cast iron pipe, pressure (50 lb.) (gas and water)	None	FS-WW-P-360a-1959
Cast iron (threaded) pipe	A40.5-1943	
Cast iron (threaded) fittings	B16.4-1963	
Cast iron drainage fittings	B16.12-1965	
Galvanized pipe and fittings	None	FS-WW-P-406(1)-1945
Malleable iron fittings (threaded)		
150 lbs.	B16.3-1963	
300 lbs.	B16.3-1963	

For notes see end of table, page 76.

Table RS16-1 (*Cont.*). **Standards for Plumbing Materials**[a]

Materials	USASI	Other
Steel pipe, seamless and welded, black and zinc coated (not intended for close coiling)	B36.20-1966	
Steel pipe, seamless and welded, black and zinc coated (suitable for close coiling)	B36.1-1966	
Stainless steel pipe	B36.19-1965	
Union, malleable iron or steel	None	FS-WW-O-531a-1957
		FS-WW-U-536(1)-1953
Wrought-iron pipe	B36.2-1966	
Valves, cast iron, gate 125 and 250 lb. threaded and flanged	None	FS-WW-V-58(1)-1956
Pipe fittings, bronze and ferrous (bushings, plugs and locknuts), threaded	None	FS-WW-P-471(1)-1946
Nipples, pipe threaded	None	FS-WW-N-351a-1956
Nonferrous Pipe and Fittings—		
Brass tube	H36.1-1967	
Brass pipe	H27.1-1963	
Brass or bronze flanges and flanged fittings, 150 and 300 lb.	B16.24-1962	
Brass or bronze screwed fittings, 125 lb. and 250 lb.	B16.15-1964	
Cast-bronze solder joint pressure fittings	B16.18-1963	
Cast-bronze solder joint drainage fittings	B16.23-1960	
Copper pipe	H26.1-1963	
Copper pipe, threadless	H26.2-1963	
Copper tube, seamless	H23.3-1965	
Water tube, copper, type K, L	H23.1-1967	
Wrought copper and wrought bronze solder joint fittings	B16.22-1963	
Wrought copper and wrought copper alloy solder joint drainage fittings	B16.29-1966	
Lead pipe and traps	None	WW-P-325-1944
Unions, brass or bronze, 250 lb.	None	FS-WW-U-516-1933
Valves, bronze; angle, check and globe, 125 and 150 lb., threaded and flanged	None	FS-WW-V-51a(2)-1954
Valves; bronze, gate, 125 and 150 lb., threaded and flanged	None	FS-WW-V-54b-1962
Pipe fittings, bronze and ferrous (bushings, plugs and locknuts), threaded	None	FS-WW-P-471(1)-1946
Nonmetallic Pipe and Fittings—		
Asbestos cement (sewer) pipe[b]	None	ASTM-C428-65T
Asbestos cement underdrain	None	ASTM-C508-67T
Clay drain tile	None	ASTM-C4-62
Concrete sewer pipe, reinforced	None	ASTM-C76-65T
Concrete sewer pipe, nonreinforced	None	ASTM-C14-67
Clay sewer pipe, standard strength	A106.3-1965	ASTM-C-13-64T

Table RS16-1 (*Cont.*). Standards for Plumbing Materials[a]

Materials	USASI	Other
Vitrified clay sewer pipe, salt-glazed, and unglazed extra strength	None	ASTM-C200-65T
Vitrified clay sewer pipe, ceramic glazed, extra strength	None	FS-SSP-361b-1962
Vitrified clay sewer pipe, perforated, standard strength	A106.1-1962	
Plumbing Fixtures—		
Drinking fountains	Z4.2-1942	
Enameled cast-iron plumbing fixtures	None	CS77-56
Earthenware (vitreous glazed) plumbing fixtures	None	CS111-43
Formed steel enameled sanitary ware	None	FS-WW-P-541b(2)-1962
Formed metal porcelain enameled-sanitary ware	None	FS-WW-P-541b(2)-1962
Heaters, water, instantaneous (steam-water converter type)	None	FS-WW-H-191-1954
Plumbing fixtures (for) land use	None	FS-WW-P-541b(2)-1962
Stainless steel plumbing fixtures	None	
Staple, vitreous china plumbing fixtures	None	CS243-62
		CS20-63
Stills, water; portable (without heating device) for U.S.P. "distilled water"	None	FS-RR-S-726(1)-1950
Porcelain-enameled tanks for domestic use	None	CS115-60
Miscellaneous Materials and Standards—		
Automatic relief valves	Z21.22-1964	
Air gap standards	A40.4-1942	
Backflow preventers	A40.6-1943	
Brass cleanout plugs	None	FS-WW-P-401(3)-1951
Brazing filler metal	None	ASTM-B260-62T
Caulking lead, Type I	None	FS-QQ-L-156(1)-1946
Caulking; lead wool and lead pig	None	FS-QQ-C-40-1963
Cement lining	A21.4-1964	
Coal-tar, enamel, protective coating	None	AWWA C203-62
Fixture setting compound	None	FS-HH-C-536a-1954
Flange dimensions, standard (classes 125 and 250 cast iron flanges, classes 150, 250 and 300 bronze flanges (land use)	None	FS-WW-F-406a(1)-1943
Galvanized iron and steel sheets	G8.2-1964	
Gaskets, plumbing-fixture-setting	None	FS-HH-G-116-1936
Hangers and supports, pipe	None	FS-WW-H-171b-1959
Resilient joints	None	ASTM-C425-64
Rubber gaskets (concrete sewer pipes)	None	ASTM-C443-65
Seal joints, sewer	None	FS-SS-S-169-1954
Sheet brass, leaded and nonleaded	None	ASTM-B36-66
		ASTM-B121-66
Sheet copper	None	ASTM-B152-60
Sheet lead, grade A	None	FS-QQ-L-201d-1961

Table RS16-1 (*Cont.*). **Standards for Plumbing Materials**[a]

Materials	USASI	Other
Solder metal	None	ASTM-B32-66T
Steel septic tanks	None	CS177-62
Domestic hot water heaters	Z21.10.1-1966	
	C72.1-1949	

NOTES FOR TABLE RS16-1

[a]Abbreviations used in the table refer to the following organizations:

USASI–United States of America Standards Institute

ASTM–American Society for Testing and Materials

AWWA–American Water Works Association

CS–Commercial Standards

FS–Federal Specifications

[b]Asbestos cement building sewer pipe shall meet the requirements of ASTM Standard C 428-65T expanded as follows:

(1) Additional sizes 4 in. and 5 in.

(2) No hydrostatic test for building sewer service

(3) Flexural strength:

Size (in.)	Length (ft.)	Class 1500	Class 2400	Class 3300
		Total flexural load, lbs.		
4	10	550	775	1100
4	13	750	1000	1350
5	10	950	1375	1900
5	13	1250	1775	2350
6	10	1500	1700	2100
6	13	2000	2200	2600

(4) Crushing strength: Include 4-in. and 5-in. for Classes 1500, 2400, 3300. Crushing test: one specimen from each 300 length of 4-in., 5-in., and 6-in. size pipes.

(2) Water distribution system pipe. Hard temper type "K" and type "L" copper tube, type "TP" threadless copper, galvanized wrought iron, galvanized steel, red brass, and approved plastic pipe. Type "L" copper tube not permitted underground. Flexible type of copper tubing not permitted.

(b) Drainage systems.—

(1) Above ground piping within buildings.—Brass, hard temper type "K" and type "L" copper tube; uncoated, extra heavy cast iron soil pipe; threaded cast iron pipe; galvanized steel; galvanized wrought iron; "D" type lead waste pipe; and approved plastic pipe. Lead waste pipe may be used, maximum of 5 ft. per fixture.

(2) Underground piping in buildings.—Uncoated, extra heavy cast iron soil pipe, brass pipe or type "K" hard temper copper tube.

(3) Building house sewers.—Uncoated, extra heavy cast iron soil pipe. Minimum of 8″ in size in Manhattan and 6″ in the other boroughs. House sewers for one- and two-family dwellings may be sized as per Table RS 16-13 for use to the curb line, and shall be of vitreous tile or asbestos cement pipe.

(4) Underground yard drainage and storm water piping.—Within the property line and away from foundation walls. Shall be uncoated, extra heavy cast iron soil pipe; asbestos cement pipe; vitreous tile pipe or concrete pipe.

(5) Chemical wastes (Acid wastes) and vents.—Separate drainage systems of AR (Acid resisting) material when pH of water is less than 4.5 or more than 9.5. Material to be silicon cast iron pipe (DURIRON), chemical lead pipe, chemical stoneware pipe, borosilicate glass pipe, or approved plastic pipe regardless of building height.

(c) Venting systems.—

(1) Above ground venting.—Same as drainage piping above ground.

(2) Underground venting.—Same as drainage piping underground.

(3) Chemical waste systems.—Vent piping to conform with requirements for chemical waste pipe.

(d) Fittings.—Material of fittings to conform to type of piping material. (Exception: Black cast iron fittings may be used with brass or galvanized pipe.) Threaded drainage fittings to be recessed type.

(e) Other piping systems and miscellaneous materials.—

(1) Roof drains.—To be of corrosion resistant material.

(2) Exterior leaders (downspouts).—To be of corrosion resistant material. Galvanized steel, galvanized wrought iron, brass, or cast iron pipe may be used for the first 15 ft. of leader extending up from grade.

(3) Sub-soil drains.—Shall be of clay tile that is open jointed, horizontally split, or perforated; open joint cast iron soil pipe; porous cement pipe; asbestos cement pipe that is open jointed, horizontally split, or perforated.

(4) Lead bends and traps.—Walls to be at least 1/8 in. thick.

(5) Sheet copper.—To weigh at least 12 ounces per sq. ft.

(6) Sheet lead.—To weigh at least 4 lbs. per sq. ft.

(7) Caulking ferrules.—Shall be of brass or copper. See Table RS 16-3.

Table RS 16-3. Caulking Ferrules*

Pipe Sizes (in.)	Inside Diam. of Ferrule (in.)	Min. Length of Ferrule (in.)	Min. Weight of Each Ferrule
2	2¼	4½	1 lb.– 0 oz.
3	3¼	4½	1 lb.-12 oz.
4	4¼	4½	2 lbs.- 8 oz.

*Ferrules may be tapped "T" or "Y" types.

(8) Soldering bushings.—Soldering bushings shall be brass or copper in accordance with Table RS 16-4.

Table RS 16-4. Soldering Bushings

Pipe Sizes (in.)	Minimum Weight of Each Ferrule
1¼	6 oz.
1½	8 oz.
2	14 oz.
2½	1 lb. 6 oz.
3	2 lbs. 0 oz.
4	3 lbs. 8 oz.

(9) Floor flanges.—Shall be of cast brass at least 1/8-in. thick, or cast iron at least 1/4-in. thick.

(10) Cleanout plugs.—Shall be of cast brass at least 1/8-in. thick. May be of nylon material in an accessible location.

(11) Flush pipes and fittings.—Shall be of nonferrous material, at least No. 22 U.S. gage.

SECTION P103.0   JOINTS AND CONNECTIONS

§P103.1   **Types of joints for piping materials.**—

(a) Asbestos cement pipe joints.—Shall be made with sleeve couplings of same material as the pipe. Sealed with approved rings.

(b) Brazed joints.—Use silver solder, with melting point OVER 1000°F.

(e) Cast iron soil pipe.—Joints to be minimum of 1-in. deep with one pouring.

(f) Cast iron water pipe.—Use asbestos rope instead of oakum.

(h) Clay sewer pipe.—Use hot poured compound or approved materials.

(i) Concrete sewer pipe.—Use hot poured compound or approved gasket rings.

(k) Copper tube (type "K" or "L").—Use silver solder joints **except in Alteration of a multiple dwelling 7 stories or less, in which 95-5 solder can be used**.

(l) Couplings.—Couplings to be used on all concealed water supply and gas piping that is threaded.

(m) Expansion joints.—To be accessible, used where required, and may be slip joints.

(s) Threaded joints.—Remove all burrs (ream pipes). Pipe joint cement to be used only on male threads.

(t) Threadless copper pipe ("TP").—Silver solder joints required.

(u) Unions.—To be ground joint.

(v) Wiped joints.–Minimum of 3/4 in. on each side of joint. Minimum of 3/8 in. thickness at thickest part. See Diagram 18.

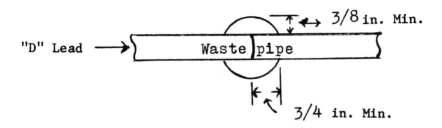

Wiped Joint.–Diagram 18.

§P103.2   **Joints between different piping material.**–

(a) Cast iron and copper tube.–Directly caulked, or by caulking ferrules.

(b) Cast iron and vitrified clay pipe.–Use bituminous compound, or a preformed bituminous ring.

(c) Copper tube and threaded pipe.–Shall be made with brass adapter fitting. Copper tube to be soldered to adapter fitting.

(d) Threaded pipe and cast iron pipe.–To be caulked or screwed.

(e) Lead and cast iron, wrought iron, steel, copper, or brass pipe.–Made by means of wiped joints to a caulking ferrule or a solder nipple.

§P103.3   **Connections between drainage piping and certain fixtures.**–Connected to water closets or other floor outlet fixtures by brass, cast iron or other approved flanges; caulked, soldered, or screwed. Bolted with an approved gasket between fixture and flange. Set on waterproof ring or slab.

§P103.4   **Tightness.**–Joints and connections to be gas and watertight, and to withstand test required.

§P103.5   **Waterproofing.**–Roof joints to be watertight. Use lead, copper, aluminum, or equivalent flashing materials.

SECTION P104.0 PLUMBING FIXTURES

§P104.1   **Requirements.**–

(a) Minimum number of fixtures.–See Table RS 16-5.

(b) Facilities for each sex.–Separate toilet or bathing facilities for each sex.

(c) Facilities for physically handicapped.–Every public building to have at least one water closet accessible for the physically handicapped, with toilet seat at least 20 in. above floor. Also provide one drinking fountain, non-recessed type, set 30 in. above floor.

Table RS 16-5. Minimum Number of Plumbing Fixtures Required[a]

Type of Building Occupancy	Type of Fixture					
	Water Closets	Urinals	Lavatories	Bathtubs or Showers	Drinking Fountains	Other Fixtures
Assembly–places of worship[b]	No. of Persons / No. of Fixtures: 150 Women — 1 300 Men — 1	No. of Persons / No. of Fixtures: 300 Men[c] — 1	1			
Assembly–other than places of worship (auditoriums, theaters, convention halls)	No. of Persons / No. of Fixtures: 1-100 — 1 101-200 — 2 201-400 — 3 Over 400, add 1 fixture for each additional 500 men and 1 for each 300 women	No. of Persons / No. of Fixtures: 1-200 — 1 201-400 — 2 401-600 — 3 Over 600, add 1 fixture for each 300 men[c]	No. of Persons / No. of Fixtures: 1-200 — 1 201-400 — 2 401-750 — 3 Over 750, add 1 fixture for each 500 persons		1 for each 1,000 persons except that there shall be at least 1 fixture at each assembly floor level or tier 1 for each 75 persons	Where motion picture projection booths contain more than 2 projectors, at least 1 water closet and 1 lavatory shall be provided on the same level and within 20 ft. of the booth
Dormitories–school or labor, also institutional	Men: 1 for each 10 persons. Women: 1 for each 8 persons.	1 for each 25 men. Over 150, add 1 fixture for each 50 men[c]	1 for each 12 persons	1 for each 8 persons. For women's dormitories 1 bathtub shall be substituted for 1 shower at the ratio of 1 for each 30 women		Laundry trays 1 for each 50 persons

(For footnotes see page 83.)

Table RS 16-5 (Continued). Minimum Number of Plumbing Fixtures Required[a]

Type of Building Occupancy	Type of Fixture					
	Water Closets	Urinals	Lavatories	Bathtubs or Showers	Drinking Fountains	Other Fixtures
Single room occupancies for sleeping accommodations only	1 for each 6 persons		1 for each 6 persons	1 for each 6 persons		
Dwellings—one- and two-family	1 for each dwelling unit		1 for each dwelling unit	1 for each dwelling unit		Kitchen sink, 1 for each dwelling unit
Public buildings, offices, business mercantile, storage; warehouses, factories, and institutional employees[d]	No. of Persons each sex / No. of Fixtures 1-15 / 1 16-35 / 2 36-55 / 3 56-80 / 4 81-110 / 5 111-150 / 6 1 fixture for each additional 40 persons	Urinals may be provided in Men's[d] toilet rooms in lieu of water closets but for not more than 1/2 of the required number of water closets when more than 35 persons	No. of Persons / No. of Fixtures 1-20 / 1 21-40 / 2 41-60 / 3 61-90 / 4 91-125 / 5 1 fixture for each additional 45 persons		1 for each 75 persons	
Schools: Elementary Secondary	Boys / Girls 1/90 / 1/35 1/90 / 1/35	1/30 boys 1/30 boys	1/50 pupils 1/50 pupils Over 300 pupils 1/100 pupils	In gym or pool shower rooms, 1/3 pupils of a largest class using pool at any one time	1/50 persons but at least 1 per floor	

Table RS 16-5 (Continued). Minimum Number of Plumbing Fixtures Required[a]

Type of Building Occupancy	Water Closets		Urinals	Lavatories	Bathtubs or Showers	Drinking Fountains	Other Fixtures
	Men 1/60	Women 1/40					
Public bathing	1/60	1/40	1/60	1/60	1/40		
Workmen's temporary facilities	1/30 workmen		1/30 workmen			At least 1 per floor equivalent for each 100 workmen	
Hospitals and Institutions	See Section P114.0						
Industrial— foundries only	No. of Persons — No. of Fixtures: 1-10 → 1; 11-25 → 2; 26-50; 51-80; 81-125. 1 additional fixture for each additional 45 persons		Where more than 10 men are employed: No. of Men[d] — No. of Urinals: 11-29 → 1; 30-79 → 2. 1 additional fixture for each additional 80 males	No. of Persons — No. of Fixtures: 1-8 → 1; 9-16 → 2; 17-30 → 3; 31-45 → 4; 46-65 → 5. 1 additional fixture for each additional 25 persons	1 shower for each 15 persons exposed to excessive heat or occupational hazard from poisonous, infectious, or irritating material	1 for each 75 persons	
Swimming pools	See Section P116.0						
Kitchens for public or employees dining				1 lavatory for the personal use of kitchen employees			One machine or a 3-compartment sink for the effective washing and sanitizing of all cutlery, dishes and glasses before re-use.

Table RS 16-5 (*Continued*). Minimum Number of Plumbing Fixtures Required[a]

Type of Building Occupancy	Type of Fixture					
	Water Closets	Urinals	Lavatories	Bathtubs or Showers	Drinking Fountains	Other Fixtures
Dwellings— multiple or apartment	1 for each dwelling unit or apartment		1 for each dwelling unit or apartment	1 for each dwelling unit or apartment		Kitchen sink— 1 for each dwelling unit or apartment. Within each dwelling unit, not designed for use by transients, one laundry tray or automatic laundry washing machine; or in a readily accessible location within a general laundry room. 1 two-compartment tray for each 10 dwelling units or 1 automatic laundry-washing machine for each 20 dwelling units.

Notes.—

[a]The population used in determining the number of fixtures required shall be based on the number of people to occupy the space but in no case shall the population be less than that determined by allowing 125 sq. ft. of net floor area per person.

[b]Such facilities may be in adjacent buildings under the same ownership or control, and shall be accessible during periods when the assembly space is occupied.

[c]Where urinals are provided for women, the same number of fixtures shall be provided *as* for men.

[d]Facilities for employees in a storage building or warehouse may be located in an adjacent building, under the same ownership, where the maximum distance of travel from the working space to the toilet facilities does not exceed 500 ft, horizontally.

(d) Accessibility.—For fixtures specified in Table RS 16-5 for public buildings. To be located not more than one floor above or one floor below for toilet use, except where passenger elevators are available.

§P104.3   **Overflows.**—To be conveyed to fixture side of trap.

§P104.4   **Water closets.**—

(a) Prohibited Types.—

(1) Washout, pan, plunger, valve, offset, latrine, and side spud.

(2) Frostproof water closets permitted by Commissioner only for temporary use.

(3) Water closets to be able to pass at least a 1 3/4-in.-diameter ball.

(b) Public water closets.—To be elongated type.

(c) Water closets for children's use.—In nurseries and schools for children under 6 years of age, to be of suitable height.

(d) Water closet seats.—Required to be of nonabsorbent material and open-front types for public use.

(e) Water closet soil pipe connections.—

(1) Lead connections.—Lead bends to be soldered to floor flanges.

(2) Iron connections.—3 in. permitted.

(3) Copper connections.—3 in. permitted.

(4) Other type connections.—Equivalent materials permitted.

(5) Reducing connections.—4 in. x 3 in. permitted.

§P104.5   **Urinals.**—

(a) Prohibited urinals.—

(1) Floor-type trough.

(2) Washdown or washout-type with integral strainers.

(b) Wall-hung trough urinals.—Permitted for temporary use only.

(d) Surrounding material.—Nonabsorbent material to be to a point 1 ft. in front of lip of urinal, 1 ft. on each side, and 4 ft. above floor.

§P104.6   **Flushing devices for water closets and urinals.**—

(a) Where required.—Flushometers or toilet tanks for water closets, urinals, or clinical sinks.

(b) Number of fixtures served.—One flushing device for each fixture, except for urinals if each one is automatically flushed.

(c) Flushometer valves.—To be accessible, to be provided with approved vacuum breaker, minimum 4 in. above overflow rim of fixture, and to have sufficient water pressure to operate.

(d) Flush tanks.—To have adequate water supply. Ball cocks to be provided with vacuum breaker, minimum 1 in. above overflow tube.

§P104.7   **Lavatories.**—

(a) Waste outlet.—Minimum 1 1/4 in. in diameter.

(b) Multiple-type fixture.—Each 18 in. of length equals one fixture.

§P104.8   **Bathtubs.**—Minimum 1 1/2 in. in diameter for waste and overflow.

§P104.9   **Showers.**—

(a) Waste outlets.—

(1) Minimum, 2 in. in diameter for waste outlets for single showers other than those in bathtubs.

(2) Minimum, 3 in. in diameter for waste outlets for a gang shower.

(b) Shower compartments.—

(1) Minimum, 900 sq. in. of floor area.

(2) Minimum, 30 lineal inches in either direction.

(c) Shower floors or receptors.—Shower pans or receptors required, except on ground.

§P104.10   **Sinks.**—

(a) Minimum, 1 1/2 in. in diameter for waste outlet.

§P104.11   **Dishwashing machines.**—

(a) General.—Requires trap.

(b) Domestic machines.—Discharge permitted to sink waste, using a 3/4 in. "Y" branch on inlet side of trap, discharge pipe to rise to above overflow level of sink.

(c) Water connections.—Air gap or vacuum breaker and check valve.

(d) Commercial machines.—

(1) Minimum 140° to 160°F wash water.

(2) Minimum 180°F rinse water.

§P104.12   **Automatic clothes washers.**—

(a) Water supply to have air gap or vacuum breaker.

(b) Domestic type.—Waste disposed through an air break to a 2-in. trap. Trap to be directly or indirectly waste connected.

(c) Commercial type.—Disposed to a trench with trapped and vented drains.

§P104.13   **Laundry trays.**—Minimum 1 1/2-inch-diameter waste outlet.

§P104.14   **Garbage can washers.**—

(a) 3-inch drain with removable basket.

(b) To have air gap or vacuum breaker and check valve for water supply line.

§P104.17   **Floor drains.**—See Diagram 26.

(a) Location.—Readily accessible.

(b) Strainers.—Open area equal to drain pipe area.

(c) Size.—Minimum 3-inch diameter outlet.

(d) Provision for evaporation.—Trap to be deep-seal type and water supply to be maximum, 3 ft. above drain.

(e) Traps.—Machinery or equipment room floor drains to be maximum, 15 ft. from trap.

§P104.18   **Drains for drip pipes.**—See Section P108.11.

§P104.19   **Funnel drains.**—For clear water waste only; traps above floor to be individually vented.

§P104.20   **Special plumbing fixtures.—**

(a) Water connections.—Baptisteries, ornamental fountains, swimming pools, etc., to be protected from back-siphonage.

(b) Water- and waste-connected specialties.—Require approval of Commissioner.

SECTION P105.0   TRAPS AND CLEANOUTS

§P105.1   **Fixture traps.—**See Diagram 19.

(a) Separate traps for each fixture.—

(1) Not more than 2 ft. (horizontally) from outlet.

(2) Not more than 4 ft. (vertically) to trap weir. See Diagram 19.

(3) No fixture to be double trapped. See Diagram 20 for exceptions.

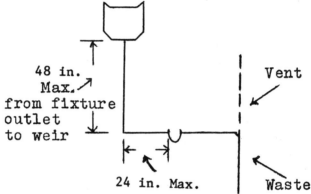

Separate Traps for Each Fixture.—Diagram 19.

Exceptions.—

(1) Fixtures with integral traps.

(2) Combination fixtures.

(3) Three compartment sink, three laundry trays, or one sink and 2 laundry trays.

(4) A domestic dishwasher drain.—Maximum of 3½ ft. from sink trap. For type of connection see Section P104.11(b).

(5) No trap for drainpipes from safety relief apparatus, condenser blow-offs, etc. For indirect waste for fixtures and equipment, trap may be omitted up to maximum 8 ft. developed length.

(b) Fixture trap sizes.—See Table RS16-6. No trap to be larger than drainage pipe.

(c) Prohibited traps.—**The only permitted types are:**

(1) Grease traps, plaster traps, etc., if approved by BS & A.

(2) "P" traps

(3) "S" traps for water closets and similar fixtures, or for floor outlet slop sinks. See Diagram 20.

(d) Design of traps.–

(1) Self cleansing, smooth waterway (except grease trap, etc.).

(2) Slip joint permitted on inlet side.

(3) Ground joint union connection permitted in trap seal.

(e) Seals.–Minimum 2 in., maximum 4 in.

(f) Setting and protection.–

(1) Level.

(2) Protected from frost.

(3) Protected from evaporation.

§P105.2   **Building (House) traps.**–

(a) Inside property line (at front wall)

(b) Sewer side of all connections **except:**

(1) Sewage ejector discharge.

(2) Oil separator discharge.

(3) Leader line on COMBINED SEWER.–(Permitted to also be connected on house side of house trap.)

(c) Accessible pit with approved cover (inside) or (outside).

(d) Handhole extensions, 18 in. maximum, from center line of pipe. See Diagram 3.

§P105.3   **Drainage pipe cleanouts.**–

(a) Location.–Within 50 ft. on horizontal drainage lines.

(b) Underground drainage.–Cleanouts to be extended to floor, grade, or wall.

(c) Every change of direction over 45 degrees, on horizontal piping.

(d) Base of stacks.–At or near base of all waste, inside leader and soil stacks.

(e) Direction of flow.–

(f) Same size as pipe.–Minimum size 4 inches for pipes 4 inches or larger.

(g) Clearance.–Accessible to clear a stoppage.

(h) Uncovered.–Accessible.

(i) Equivalent cleanouts.–For removable fixtures or traps. No more than 90 degree angle to be rodded.

§P105.4   **Interceptors, Separators, and Neutralizing Pits.**–

(a) Interceptors required.–For oil, grease, sand, and other harmful substances to drainage system and public sewer, as per rules of Department of Public Works.

(b) Interceptors not required.–For individual dwelling units.

(c) Separators required.–At repair garages, gasoline stations with grease pits or racks, and factories producing oily or flammable liquid waste. Provide a sand interceptor for auto laundries. No oil separator required.

(d) Grease interceptors.–

(1) Commercial building.–Grease interceptor required for waste from pot sinks, scullery sinks, food scrap sinks, scraper section of commercial

Table RS16-6. Minimum Size of Fixture Traps for Various Types of Plumbing Fixtures

Fixture	Trap Size[a] (in.)
Bathtub (with or without overhead shower)	1½
Bidets (see Section P107.13)	1½
Combination sink and wash (laundry) tray	2
Dental unit or cuspidor	1½
Drinking fountain	1½
Dishwasher, commercial	2
Dishwasher, domestic	1½
Floor drain	3
Funnel drain	1½
Kitchen sink, domestic	2
Laboratory, cup sink	1½
Laboratory, sink	2
Lavatory, common	1½[b]
Lavatory, barber shop, beauty parlor or surgeon's	1½
Lavatory, multiple type (wash fountain or wash sink)	1½
Laundry tray (1 or 2 compartments)	1½
Shower, stall	2
Shower, gang	3
Sink (surgeon's)	1½
Sink (flushing rim type, flush valve supplies)	3
Sink (service type with trap standard)	3
Sink, commercial (pot, scullery, or similar type)	2
Sterilizers	1½
Urinal (pedestal)	3
Urinal (stall type)	2
Urinal (wall lip type)	2
Urinal (women's)	3
Water closet (waste outlet)	3

Notes. –
[a]Size of outlet, the inlet size of trap same as outlet from fixture.
[b]Size of three lavatory equivalents–2 in. for more than three.

dishwashers, and floor drains receiving spillage from soup or stock kettles. EXCEPTION.—No rinse water of 180°F, or higher, to enter a grease trap (such as a dishwasher discharge line).

(2) Number of grease interceptors.—One interceptor shall be permitted for all fixtures requiring the interceptor, provided it is individually trapped and vented, and an additional vent is installed at the interceptor, and provided the size of the interceptor is sufficient to accommodate all of the fixtures connected thereto.

(3) Use as a trap.—The interceptor may be used in lieu of an individual fixture trap if the developed length from the fixture outlet to the inlet of the interceptor is not more than 48". See Diagram 20.

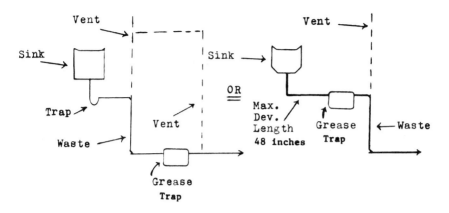

Grease Interceptor.—Diagram 20. Two Methods.

　(4) Capacity.—For specific details see Building Code.
　(5) Material.—All prefabricated grease interceptors shall be approved.
　(e) Oil and flammable liquids separator.—
　　(1) Separation of liquids.—Separates oil and water.
　　(2) Design of separator.—See Building Code for specific details.
　　(3) Venting.—See Section P105.6.
　　(4) Connection to sewer.—On sewer side of house trap.
　　(5) Oil storage tank.—Available for oil removed from separator.
§P105.5　**Interceptors, Separators, and Neutralizing Pits for Specific Services.**—
　(a) Sand interceptors.—(Commercial) To be accessible and have 6-in. minimum water seal. See Diagram 25.
　(b) Laundries.—(Commercial) To prevent solids, rags, etc., 1/2 in. in diameter or larger, from entering drainage system. Interception within a trough will be permitted.
　(c) Bottling establishments.—To prevent broken glass, etc., from entering drainage system.
　(d) Slaughter houses.—To have necessary interceptors or separators.
　(e) Laboratories, dyeworks, chemical plants, etc.—When discharging drainage of pH below 4.5 or above 11.5, such wastes to be neutralized, as per rules of Department of Public Works.
§P105.6　**Venting of Interceptors, Separators, and Neutralizing Pits.**—
　(a) Oil interceptors, separators.—
　　(1) Drainage and vent system to be independent of any other system.
　　(2) Independent 3-in. vent line from top of separator to at least 12 ft. above street level.
　　(3) Connection to be on sewer side of house trap or connected directly to sewer.

(4) No house trap required for separator. Can be used instead of trap.

(5) Separate fresh-air inlet. **Same rule as regular house drain.** See Section P108.5.

(6) At least one 3-in. stack through roof.

(b) Neutralizing pits and interceptors (OTHER THAN OIL).—Vents may connect to sanitary venting system.

§P105.7   **Accessibility of Interceptors, Separators, and Neutralizing Pits.—** To be accessible for removing cover, and for maintenance.

§P105.8   **Maintenance of Interceptors, Separators, and Neutralizing Pits.—** If not cleaned and properly maintained, revocation of Industrial Waste permit possible, by Department of Public Works.

§P105.9   **Backwater valves.—**

(a) Fixtures and area drains.—

(1) Permitted for one fixture subject to backflow.

(2) Permitted for group of fixtures subject to backflow.

(3) Permitted at street side of house trap.

(b) Design.—

(1) To have same opening as pipe.

(2) Bearing parts of corrosion resistant metal.

(3) Approved type.

§P105.10   **Industrial wastes sampling manholes.—**For specific details, see Building Code.

SECTION P106.0 HANGERS AND SUPPORTS

§P106.1   **Material.—**Metal or equivalent material for proper support. Piers may be concrete, brick, or equivalent material.

§P106.2   **Attachment to building.—**Securely, and at proper intervals.

§P106.3   **Intervals of supports.—**

(a) Vertical piping.—

(1) Cast iron soil pipe, at base and each story. Maximum interval, 20 ft.

(2) Threaded pipe, at every other story. Maximum interval, 25 ft.

(3) Copper tube, at each story.

(4) Other materials, as required for structural stability.

(b) Horizontal piping.—

(1) Cast iron soil pipe, every 5 ft. and behind every hub.

(2) Threaded pipe, 1″ or less—8-ft. intervals.

(3) Threaded pipe, 1 1/4″ or over—12-ft. intervals.

(4) Copper tubing, 1 1/4″ or less—6-ft. intervals.

(5) Copper tubing, 1 1/2″ or more—10-ft. intervals.

(6) Other materials.—As required for structural stability.

(c) Base of stacks.—To be properly supported.

SECTION P107.0 WATER SUPPLY AND DISTRIBUTION

§P107.1 **Permits.—**

(a) Permits, inspection and approval for WATER SERVICE PIPING shall be obtained from the Department of Water Supply, Gas and Electricity. Water Service Piping.—That portion of the water supply system extending from the public street water main to the house control valve inside the building, or to a point where the supply is fully metered. See Diagram 16.

(b) Permits for sidewalk and street openings.—Shall be obtained from the Department of Highways.

§P107.2 **Water service.—(No jurisdiction by Department of Buildings.)**

(a) Taps to city water mains.—See Rules of the Department of Water Supply, Gas and Electricity in appendix at end of the book.

(b) Service.—

(1) Service pipes-definition.—See Section P107.1 and Diagram 16.

(2) Size of taps and water service.—**For method of computation** see Tables to be Used for the Determination of the Size of Service Pipe and Taps in appendix at end of the book.

For additional items in this section.—**(No jurisdiction by Department of Buildings.)** See Rules of the Department of Water Supply, Gas and Electricity in appendix at end of the book.

§P107.3 **Meters.—(No jurisdiction by Department of Buildings.)** See Rules of the Department of Water Supply, Gas and Electricity in appendix at end of the book.

§P107.4 **Check valves.—**

(a) A check valve is required:

(1) Where a building is supplied by services connected to different water mains.

(2) Where there is a possibility of backflow from tanks, siamese connections, or other apparatus or fixtures within the building.

(b) Such check valve to be placed within 2 ft. of outlet side of main house control valve; or if building is metered, shall be between meter test tee and outlet valve. For Diagram of "Typical Meter Setting," see Rules of the Department of Water Supply, Gas and Electricity in appendix at end of the book.

§P107.5 **Water supply distribution system.—**

(a) Design, adjustment, and maintenance.—Pipe sizing to be designed for satisfactory performance by an architect or engineer, subject to the approval of the Commissioner.

(b) Minimum pressure.—

(1) 8 psi near faucet or wide open outlet.

(2) When more pressure required, as at a flush valve, sufficient pressure to be available for satisfactory performance.

(3) System to be designed for <u>minimum pressure</u> available (during "<u>peak load</u>" hours).

(c) <u>Inadequate water pressure in street mains.</u>—Use **auxiliary water supply.** See Section P107.7.

(d) <u>Maximum pressures.</u>—Excess of 85 psi at <u>plumbing fixtures</u> requires <u>pressure reducing valves.</u>

(e) <u>Minimum size of water supply branches and risers.</u>—

(1) Velocity not to exceed 8 fps in individual fixture branch. See Table RS 16-7.

(2) Velocity not to exceed 8 fps for branches, risers, and distribution mains. "Method of Computation" in appendix at end of the book.

(f) <u>Water hammer.</u>—

(1) Use <u>approved</u> accessible air chamber at front wall. See Diagram in Rule 180 of the Rules of the Department of Water Supply, Gas and Electricity in appendix at end of the book.

Table RS16-7. Minimum Rate-of-Flow and Minimum Required Pressure During Flow for Sizing Individual Branch Supplies for Plumbing Fixtures

Location	Flow Pressure[a] (psi)	Flow Rate[b] (gpm)
Ordinary basin faucet	8	2.0
Self-closing basin faucet	8	2.5
Sink faucet, 3/8 in.	8	4.5
Sink faucet, 1/2 in.	8	4.5
Bathtub	8	5.0
Laundry-tub cock 1/2 in.	8	5.0
Shower	8	5.0
Ball cock for closet	8	3.0
Flushometer valve for closet	10–20	15–40[c]
Flushometer valve for urinal	10	15.0
Drinking fountains	....	0.75

Notes:—

[a]The flow pressure is the pressure in the supply pipe, near the faucet or water outlet while the faucet or water outlet is wide open and flowing.

[b]At fixtures supplied with both hot and cold water, the flow rate indicated is for each of the two connections.

[c]The wide range is due to the variation in designs and types of water closet flush valves and water closets.

(2) Air chambers installed at individual fixtures need not be accessible. Air chambers for fixtures shall be at least 12 in. long and of the same diameter as the branch pipe connection; for quick closing valves the chamber shall be at least 18 in. long. One air chamber may service a battery of fixtures provided the single air chamber is at least 24 in. long and is at least the size of the supply branch.

(3) Mechanical devices shall be used in accordance with the manufacturer's specifications as to location and method of installation. See Diagram 21.

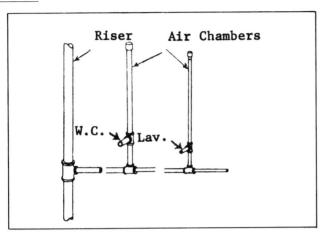

Air Chamber.—Diagram 21.

§P107.6   **Water supply control valves.**—

(a) Stop- and waste-valves prohibited. Underground or buried.

(b) Riser valves.—Valve required at foot of each riser, except one-family dwelling. In multistory building a valve is required at top of downfeed risers.

(c) Valves in dwelling units.—In two-family dwellings and group J-2 buildings (see Table 3-2), control valves required on the supply branch or stop valves on each individual fixture.

(d) Individual fixture valves.—In buildings other than in (c) above, supply valve can control each fixture or branch for each room.

(e) Tank controls.—Valves to be located at tank in tank room.

(f) Water heating equipment valve.—Cold water supply valve to be at equipment and relief valve as per Section P107.26.

(g) Accessibility.—Control valves to be accessible.

(h) Control valve design.—At least 85 percent area of pipe served.

§P107.7   **Auxiliary water systems.**—

(a) When required.—For inadequate pressure. (See Section P107.5) use:

(1) Gravity water-supply tank.

(2) Hydropneumatic pressure booster system.

(3) Water pressure booster pump system.

(4) Combination of these systems.

(5) Other systems designed by an architect or engineer, approved by Commissioner.

§P107.8   **Water supply tanks.–**

(a) Overflows.–For gravity or suction tanks.

(1) For overflow pipe sizes, see Table RS 16-8, Table RS 16-9, and Fig. RS 16-1.

(2) To discharge within 6 inches above roof or over an open water supplied fixture.

(b) Water piping control and location.–To prevent overflow of tank by

(1) Ball cock.

(2) Other automatic supply valve, or

(3) Emergency electrical cut-off.

(4) 4-inch minimum AIR GAP between water supply and overflow.

(5) Outlet.–Minimum of 2 inches above inside of tank, and to have a strainer.

(6) Downfeed to have a check valve.

(c) Drain pipes for emptying tanks.–As per rules of overflow pipes, minimum 4-inch diameter.

(d) Prohibited location.–Under any soil or waste piping.

(e) Design.–Wood, steel, or equivalent material. See Diagram 22A.

(f) Hydropneumatic pressure booster tanks.–

(1) To be cylindrical.

(2) Be built in accordance with ASME Boiler Code 1967, Section VIII.

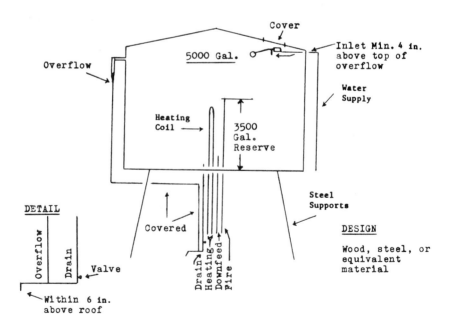

House Supply Tank.–Diagram 22A.

(3) Have a pressure relief valve.

(4) Have a vacuum relief valve if drainage possible by a fixture located below tank. See Diagram 22B.

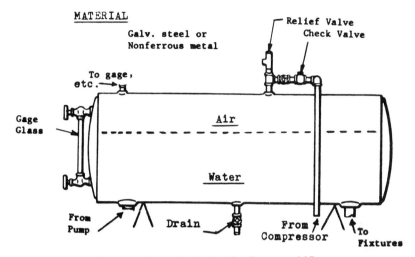

Hydropneumatic Pressure Tank (Cylindrical).—Diagram 22B.
See Section P107.8(f).

(g) Cleaning or painting tank.—
  (1) Potable water tank cleaning.—
    (a) Tank with potable water cannot be cleaned or painted with anything that will have an objectionable effect on the water.
    (b) No lead paint to be used.
  (2) Potable water tank disinfecting procedure:
    (a) Clean tank with hypochlorite solution containing minimum of 100 parts per million.
    (b) Refill tank with water, using hypochlorite while filling. Minimum of 10 parts per million.
    (c) The chlorinated water to be allowed to remain in tank for two hours.
    (d) The tank to be drained completely before refilling.
  (h) Tank supports.—As per rules of the Building Code.
  (i) Tank covers.—All water supply tanks to be covered.
§P107.9   **House and booster pumps.**—This section fully stated in the Rules of the Department of Water Supply, Gas and Electricity. (Rule 181 in appendix at end of the book.)

  (a) Directly off street main.—When pump capacity is over 400 gpm a suction tank is required.

Table RS16-8. Size of Overflows for Gravity and Suction Tanks
(See Fig. RS16-1, A and B)

Overflow Pipe Size (in.)	Maximum Allowable gpm for Each Orifice Opening into Tank	Maximum Allowable gpm for Vertical Overflow (Piping Connecting Orifices)
2	19	25
3	43	75
4	90	163
5	159	296
6	257	472
8	505	1,020
10	890	1,870
12	1,400	2,967

(b) Suction tank.—

(1) As per rule of water supply tanks. See Section P107.8.

(2) Not required for fire service unless fire service line is equal to or larger than street water main.

(c) Suction tank size.—See Table RS 16-10.

(d) Fill line to tank.—To have a flow control for water make-up.

(e) Low pressure cut-off required on booster pumps.—Installed to prevent pressure drop of over 7 psi.

(f) Check valve required.—Check valve and gate valve required at discharge of each pump.

Table RS16-9. Size of Weirs for Gravity and Suction Tanks
(See Fig. RS16-1, C)

Slotted Weir Opening into Tank between Overflow Chamber and Water Compartment*	Maximum gpm Allowable for Weir
3 in. x 24 in.	381
3½ in. x 24 in.	475
4½ in. x 24 in.	685
4½ in. x 36 in.	1,037
6 in. x 36 in.	1,569
6 in. x 48 in.	2,100

*Note.—Bottom of the overflow chamber must be at least 6 inches below weir. Bottom outlet shall be provided in the chamber of sizes based on capacities as indicated in Table RS16-8.

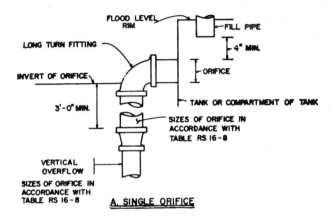

A. SINGLE ORIFICE

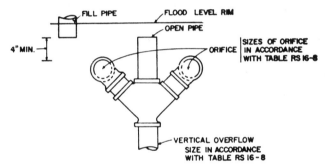

B. MULTIPLE ORIFICE

METHOD OF CONNECTING OVERALL
OVERFLOW FROM GRAVITY HOUSE AND SUCTION
WATER SUPPLY TANKS

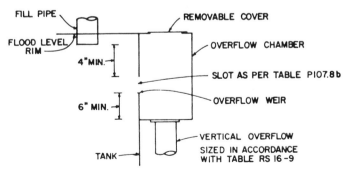

C. OVERFLOW WEIR

Fig. RS 16-1. Single and multiple overflows and overflow weir.

§P107.10   **Protection of potable water supply.**—To prevent contamination. Where well water or other unsafe water is used in a building with City water supply, piping should be kept separated and pipes to be tagged SAFE WATER and UNSAFE WATER. For more specific details see Building Code.

Table RS16-10. Suction Tank Sizes

Total Connected Pump Capacity (gpm)	Tank Capacity (gal.)
400–500	(7,500)
501 and over	(10,000)

§P107.11   **Toxic materials and substances.**—Not permitted to add materials to potable water for "taste," "odor," or to produce "toxic condition."

§P107;12   **Used piping.**—Pipe used for other purposes cannot be used for potable water supply piping.

§P107.13   **Prohibited connections to fixtures and equipment.**—
IMPORTANT. No direct water supply permitted to the following type fixtures. AIR GAP REQUIRED, **regardless** of use of check valve or vacuum breaker.
   (1) Bidets
   (2) Aspirators, injectors, water siphons, etc.
   (3) Mortuary, dissection, operating, embalming tables, etc.
   (4) Sterilizers
   (5) Flushing rim floor drains.

§P107.14   **Connections to mechanical equipment and systems.**—Potable water supply connections to boiler feed water systems and heating and cooling systems shall be made through a fixed AIR GAP. Where the equipment or system is fed through an injector the potable water shall be supplied through a fixed AIR GAP to the suction tank of a booster pump.
   FOR EXCEPTION see Department of Buildings DIRECTIVE No. 18 of 1969.

§P107.15   **Refrigeration unit condensers and cooling jackets.**—(As per Rules of the Department of Water Supply, Gas and Electricity, in appendix at end of the book.)
   (a) Installation of refrigeration and air-conditioning equipment requires a permit.
   (b) Installation of refrigeration and air-conditioning equipment requires a check valve.
   (c) Installation of refrigeration and air-conditioning equipment with over 20 pounds of refrigerant requires a relief valve set 5 psi above maximum pressure, and to be located between refrigeration unit and check valve.

<u>**DIRECTIVE NO. 18 of 1969**</u>

December 8, 1969

To: Borough Superintendents; Chief Andrea, Boiler Division

From: Thomas V. Burke, Director of Operations

Subject: Water Supply Connection Between Boilers
          Reference Standard 16 - Section P107.14

The provisions of Section P107.14 of Reference Standard 16 require that a fixed air gap be provided between the water supply system and the boiler feed water system.

The following exceptions to this requirement shall be permitted, provided the boiler capacity does not exceed 350,000 B.T.U.s per hour:-

1. A fixed air gap shall not be required for feed water connections that are arranged to be manually controlled. Such manual control consists of a stop valve in the water line, which remains closed at all times except when feed water is being supplied to the boiler, so that back siphonage cannot occur.

2. In a hot water heating system for supplying heat to a building, where the feed water is automatically supplied to the boiler, a check valve and a vacuum breaker may be substituted for the fixed air gap. An indirect connection from the vacuum breaker to a sink or a floor drain shall be provided.

In all other installations a fixed air gap shall be provided between the water supply system and the boiler.

Thomas V. Burke
Thomas V. Burke
Director of Operations

TVB/df

CC: Executive Staff
     Industry

§P107.16 **Air conditioning and refrigeration.**—All items in this section are mainly the concern of, and require the APPROVAL of the Department of Water Supply, Gas and Electricity. (See "Rule No. 177 A, B, and C" of the Rules of the Department of Water Supply, Gas and Electricity, in appendix at end of the book.)

§P107.17 **Used water return prohibited.**—NOT permitted to be returned to POTABLE water supply system. To be discharged to a fixture drain with an air break.

§P107.18 **Protection against backflow and back-siphonage.**—Install and maintain at each potable water outlet, one of the following:

(1) AIR GAP

(2) Accessible VACUUM BREAKER.

§P107.19 **Approval of devices.**—Approved equipment to be used to prevent backflow or back-siphonage.

§P107.20 **Protection of potable water supply outlets.**—

(a) All submerged inlets **except** water closet and urinal flushometers and tank ball cocks, to have a check valve between fixture and vacuum breaker.

(b) Type required.—

(1) Connections not subject to back pressure.—Nonpressure type vacuum breaker to be installed on discharge side of last valve on line serving fixture or equipment. For list of conditions, see Table RS 16-11.

(2) Connections subject to back pressure.—Where potable water connection is made to fixture, tank, vat, pump, etc., subject to backflow or back-siphonage, a pressure type vacuum breaker and check valve to be installed.

§P107.21 **Preheating apparatus.**—Water supply lines to water preheating apparatus utilizing waste water from the plumbing system shall be equipped with a vacuum breaker located at least 4 in. above the highest elevation of the preheating apparatus or coil, with a check valve between the vacuum breaker and the preheating apparatus. Any hot water boiler supplied through such preheating device and having an independent cold water supply line shall have the cold water supply line equipped with a vacuum breaker and check valve located at least 4 in. above the highest elevation of the boiler.*

§P107.23 **Chemical solution tanks or apparatus.**—Direct water supply connections to any tank or apparatus containing any chemical shall be prohibited unless specifically approved by the Department of Health.

---

*NOTE.—The BS & A ruling in pamphlet 835-38 SR, effective July 2, 1956, **disagrees** with the above Section P107.21 of the Building Code. On the third line the Building Code states **4 inches**; the BS & A ruling states **4 feet**.

Table RS16-11. Cross-Connections Where Protective Devices are Required and Critical Level (C-L) Setting for Vacuum Breakers

Fixture or Equipment	Method of Installation
Dental units	On models without built-in vacuum breakers—C-L at least 4 inches above flood rim of bowl.
Dishwashing machines	An air gap or with the C-L at least 4 inches above flood level of machine. Install on both hot and cold water supply line and on water supply to detergent or water-softening appliances.
Flushometers (closet and urinal)	C-L at least 4 inches above top of fixture supplied.
Garbage-can cleaning machine	C-L at least 4 inches above flood level of machine. Install on both hot and cold water supply lines.
Hose outlets (except outside sill cocks, drain cocks at base of water risers or at equipment, and fire hose outlets)	C-L at least 4 inches above highest point on hose line or as permitted by the Commissioner.
Laundry machines	C-L at least 4 inches above flood level of machine. Install on both hot and cold water supply lines.
Lawn sprinklers	C-L at least 12 inches above highest sprinkler or discharge outlet. Installed on header at building wall.
Steam tables	C-L at least 4 inches above floor level.
Tanks and vats	C-L at least 6 inches above flood level rim or line.
Trough urinals	C-L at least 30 inches above perforated flush pipe.
Flush tanks	All flush tanks operated by ball cocks shall have a vacuum breaker located not less than 1 inch above the overflow outlet of the flush tank.

§P107.24   **Bedpan washers.**—Require flushometer and vacuum breaker. If no flushometer used, vacuum breaker and check valve required. Approved steam connection may be used.

§P107.25   **Laboratory outlets.**—Serrated tip or hose end requires a vacuum breaker.

§P107.26   **Hot water supply system.**—

(a) Return circulation – where required.—

(1) Building 4 stories or more in height, or

(2) Developed length of hot water piping from source of supply to farthest fixture exceeds 50 ft.

(b) Pressure relief valve, temperature relief valve, or combination pressure and temperature relief valve required at hot water heating equipment.—

(1) No check valve permitted between safety device and hot water equipment.

(2) Outlets of relief valves not permitted to be connected to drainage or vent piping.

(3) Relief discharge pipe to be same size as valve discharge connection. Pipe to terminate with unthreaded end.

(4) Where a relief outlet discharges into a plumbing fixture, a minimum air break shall be provided.

(c) Pressure relief valves.—Set at least 25 psi above working pressure. (NOTE. Relief valves usually are set for less than 25 psi above working pressure.)

(d) Temperature relief valves.—To be immersed into hottest water.

(e) Emergency energy cut-off devices.—Approved safety devices to be installed to be able to cut off main fuel supply.

(f) Vacuum relief valves.—Required for copper lined tank that has hot water supply fixtures below tank.

(g) Pressure marking of hot water storage tank.—Shall be permanently marked in a readily accessible place stating the maximum allowable working pressure, which shall be not more than 2/3 of the bursting pressure of the tank.

(h) Temperature limit controls.—All hot water heaters and storage tanks to be so supplied.

(i) Prohibited locations and usage of hot water generators.—No solid or liquid fuel or gas-fired water heater to be installed in bedroom, bathroom, or space with less than 300 cubic feet volume. Gas equipment vents not to be used for solid or liquid fuel-fired equipment.

§P107.27   **Disinfection of potable water systems.**—Method and sampling as per Department of Health and rules of the Building Code. For specific details see Building Code.

SECTION P108.0 SANITARY DRAINAGE PIPING

§P108.1   **Permits.**—Obtained from the Department of Buildings and Department of Public Works.

(1) From building to street line.—Jurisdiction of Department of Buildings.

(2) From street line to Public Sewer.—Jurisdiction of Department of Public Works.

§P108.2   **Street sewer connections.**—

(a) Connection not permitted within 6" of inner top of sewer.

(b) 45 degree angle connection to sewer.

(c) Inspected by Department of Public Works.

(d) Connection shall be flush with the inside face of the wall of the street sewer.

(e) No building sewer connections shall be made to catch basins or drain inlets.

§P108.3   **Abandonment of existing building sewer connections.**—

(a) To be securely sealed inside curb line.

§P108.4   **Building (House) traps.**—

(a) See Section P105.2.

(b) No house trap required for sewage ejector or sump pit inlet.

§P108.5   **Fresh air inlets.**—Required for sanitary or combined house drain, sewage ejector or oil separator.

(a) At least one-half the size of house drain, 3-inch minimum diameter.

(b) To outer air; minimum, 6 inches above grade.

(c) To have perforated plate with ventilating area equal to pipe, or a return bend with open area, minimum, 6 inches above grade.

(d) To be upstream within 4 ft. of house trap. See Diagram 23.

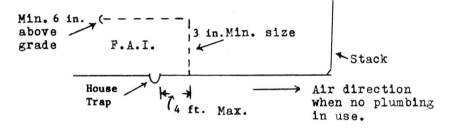

Fresh Air Inlet.—Diagram 23.

§P108.6   **Drainage below sewer level.**—

(a) Parts not draining into the gravity system.—

(1) To be lifted by approved means.

(2) The discharge from an airtight and vented sump to connect to street side of gravity house trap.

(3) Fresh air inlet required on inlet side of sewage ejector.

(4) No house trap required for a sewage ejector.

(5) The discharge from a sump not airtight and vented can connect to house drain or house sewer.

(b) Drainage and vent piping for sub-house drainage systems to be installed in same manner as for gravity systems.

(c) Sump pits or receiving tanks receiving the discharge from the sanitary drainage system or from the sub-house sanitary drainage system.

(1) Shall be airtight and provided with a vent.

(2) Need not be airtight and vented if receiving only clear water from floor drain or machinery drips.

(d) Vents from sewage ejector tanks.—

(1) To be sized on basis of one fixture unit for each gpm flow of discharge pumps.

(2) Developed length of vent to be figured as per Table RS 16-14.

(3) Receiving tank (except Pneumatic Tank) vent may connect to gravity drainage vent system if such vent system is 3 inches or larger. See Diagram 24.

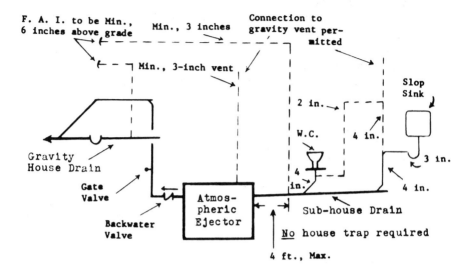

Sewage Ejector.—Diagram 24.

    (e) Relief devices of a pneumatic sewage ejector system.—
    (1) Sewage to be discharged by air pressure.
    (2) Device to have pipes, valves, and equipment to empty pot in 10 seconds.
    (3) Minimum size of pipes, valves, and equipment to be 1 1/4 inches.
    (4) To have independent vent minimum 3 inches through roof as regular vent lines.
    (f) Sump pit or ejector may be made of concrete.
    (g) A check valve and gate valve required for each sewage ejector or sump discharge.

§P108.7   **Sub-soil drainage.**—Where discharging to a public sewer.
    (a) To discharge into a sand trap.
    (b) If connected to house drain use accessible approved backwater valve.
    (c) To discharge behind a leader or area drain trap.
    (d) See Section P110.2.
    (e) If connected to Public Sewer, silt or sand interceptor to be designed by an Architect or Engineer. See Diagram 25.

§P108.8   **Drainage piping installation.**—
    IMPORTANT.—
    (a) Pitch of horizontal drainage piping.—Horizontal drainage piping shall be installed in uniform alignment at uniform slopes as follows:

Size of Piping	Minimum Slope
2 in. or less	¼ in. per ft.
Over 2 in.	1/8 in. per ft.

(b) Change of direction.—

(1) Changes in direction in drainage piping shall be made by the appropriate use of 45 degrees wyes; long sweeps; short sweeps; quarter, sixth, eighth, or sixteenth bends; or by a combination of these or equivalent fittings.

(2) Sanitary tees and quarter bends may be used in drainage lines only where the direction of flow is from the horizontal to the vertical.

(3) Short sweeps will be permitted in drainage piping 3 in. in diameter or larger for any offsets either horizontal or vertical.

(c) Prohibited fittings and connections.—

(1) No running threads, bands, or saddles shall be used in drainage or vent piping. No drainage or vent pipes shall be drilled or tapped.

(2) No fitting permitted with hub facing downstream; no double hub permitted; no Tee branch permitted for drainage.

(3) No heel or side inlet quarter bend to be used as a vent in a side or horizontal position.

(4) (a) Approved 3″ x 4″ lead bends permitted.

(b) 4″ x 3″ floor flanges permitted for 3″ lead bends.

(d) Dead ends.—A dead end is permitted as an extension for an accessible cleanout. See Diagram 4.

(e) Future drainage and vent outlets permitted if not installed as a dead end.

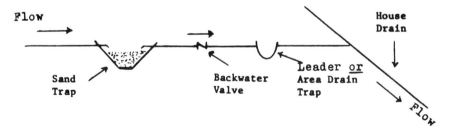

Sub-soil Drainage.—Diagram 25.

§P108.9 **Sanitary drainage fixture units.**—

(a) Value for fixtures.—For fixture unit values see Table RS 16-12 for sizing drainage and vent piping.

(b) Value for continuous or semicontinuous flow.—For fixture unit value such as a pump, air conditioner, etc., one FIXTURE UNIT equals one gpm.

Table RS16-12. Sanitary Drainage Fixture Unit Values*

Fixture or Group	Fixture Unit Value
Automatic clothes washer (2 in. standpipe)	3
Bathroom group consisting of a lavatory, bathtub or shower stall, and a water closet (direct flushometer valve)	8
Bathroom group consisting of a lavatory, bathtub or shower stall, and a water closet (flush tank)	6
Bathtub with or without overhead shower	2
Combination sink and wash tray	3
Dental unit or cuspidor	1
Dental lavatory	1
Drinking fountain	½
Dishwasher, domestic type	2
Floor drain	2
Kitchen sink, domestic type	2
Lavatory	1
Lavatory (barber shop, beauty parlor or surgeon's)	2
Lavatory, multiple type (wash fountain or wash sink), per each equivalent lavatory unit or set of faucets	2
Laboratory cup sink	1
Laboratory sink	2
Laundry tray (1 or 2 compartment)	2
Shower stall	2
Showers (group) per head	2
Sink (surgeon's)	3
Sink (flushing rim type, direct flush valve)	6
Sink (service type with trap standard)	3
Sink (service type with P trap)	2
Sink (pot, scullery, or similar type)	4
Urinal (1 in. flush valve) pedestal	6
Urinal (¾ in. flush valve) stall or wall hung	4
Urinal (flush tank)	4
Water closet (direct flush valve)	6
Water closet (flush tank)	4
Unlisted fixture, 1¼ in. fixture drain and 1½ in. trap size	1
Unlisted fixture, 1½ in. fixture drain or trap size	2
Unlisted fixture, 2 in. fixture drain or trap size	3
Unlisted fixture, 2½ in. fixture drain or trap size	4
Unlisted fixture, 3 in. fixture drain or trap size	5
Unlisted fixture, 4 in. fixture drain or trap size	6

*Note.—See Section P108.9 (b) for method of computing unit values for devices with continuous or semicontinuous flows.

§P108.10   **Sizing the sanitary drainage piping.—**

(a) Drainage piping.—For pipe sizes see Table RS 16-13, using fixture unit values of Table RS 16-12.

(b) Sewer piping.—When more than one building discharges into a **private sewer**, minimum of 3 fps permitted.

(c) Minimum size of soil and waste stacks.—

(1) Not to be smaller than branch entering it.

(2) EXCEPTION. 4″ x 3″ connection for water closet permitted.

(d) Provision for future fixtures.—Allow for additional fixture units.

(e) Minimum size of underground drainage piping.—

(1) 2″ minimum diameter.

(2) 1″ minimum drip pipes permitted if of copper or brass.

(f) Sizing of offsets in drainage piping.—

(1) Offsets of 45 degrees or less from the vertical.—May be sized as a vertical stack.

(2) Offsets of more than 45 degrees from the vertical.—

(a) The portion of the stack above the highest offset to be sized as required for a regular stack based on the total number of fixture units above the offset.

(b) The offset shall be sized as required for a building house drain. See Table RS 16-13.

Table RS16-13. Maximum Permissible Loads for Sanitary Drainage Piping
(in terms of fixture units)

Pipe Diameter (in.)	Any Horizontal Fixture, Branch, or at One Story of Stack	Total for Stack	House Building Drain, and Building Branches from Stacks			
			Slope (in. per ft.)			
			1/16	1/8	1/4	1/2
$1\frac{1}{2}$[a]	3	4	np	np	np	np
2[a]	6	8	np	np	21	26
$2\frac{1}{2}$[a]	12	30	np	np	24	31
3	20[b]	97[b]	np	20[b]	27[b]	36[b]
4	160	507	np	180	216	250
5	360	1445	np	390	480	575
6	...	2918	np	700	840	1000
8	...	6992	1440	1600	1920	2300
10	...	...	2500	2900	3500	4200
12	...	...	3900	4600	5600	6700

Notes.—
[a] No water closets permitted.
[b] Not over two water closets permitted.
np = not permitted.
Note:— **2 water closets permitted on a 3-inch stack or branch at one story.**

(c) The portion of the stack below the offset shall be sized the same as the offset or based on the total number of fixture units on the entire stack, whichever is larger.

(d) Relief vent for offset.—Install as provided in Section P109.9. No horizontal branch drain connection permitted within 2 ft. above or 2 ft. below offset. See Fig. RS 16-6.

(3) Offsets above highest branch.—A horizontal offset in a stack vent to be of a non-scaling material. (Galvanized pipe may be used.)

(4) Offsets below lowest branch.—

a. Offset of 45-degree angle, or less, from vertical. No change in pipe size required.

b. Offset of over 45-degree angle from vertical.

c. Pipe size to be figured as per house drain. See Table RS 16-13.

(5) Offsets prohibited.—No offsets on soil or waste line above any equipment used to prepare or store food unless protected by a waterproof copper pan.

§P108.11   **Drip pipes.**—Drips from pump bases, air conditioning drips, and similar clear water drips may be collected into a one-inch pipe, and the pipe may be connected to the inlet side of a floor drain trap. Underground piping shall be of brass or copper.

SECTION P109.0   VENT PIPING

§P109.1   **Size of vents.**—As per developed length and fixture units. See Table RS 16-14.

(a) Individual vent.—1 1/2 inches or 1/2 the diameter of the drainage pipe to which it is connected, whichever is greater.

(b) Relief vent.—1 1/2 inches or 1/2 the diameter of the soil or waste branch to which it is connected, whichever is greater.

(c) Branch vents.—Computed by developed length and fixture units and sized as per Table RS 16-14. See Fig. RS 16-2 for EXAMPLE.

(d) Vent stacks.—Computed by developed length from the base to the topmost termination, and sized as per Table RS 16-14.

§P109.2   **Protection of trap seals.**—The protection of trap seals from siphonage or back pressure.—By stacks, vents, back vents, continuous vents, etc. Maximum pressure differential, 1 in. of water permitted.

§P109.3   **Vent stack and stack vents.**—

(a) Minimum size.—**At least one 4-inch stack** or stack vent carried full size **through roof.**

(b) Vent stack required.—To have at least one 4-inch stack through roof. A vent stack required for each soil or waste stack containing 3 or more branch connections. Only one vent stack may serve two soil or waste stacks.

Table RS16-14. Size of Vent Stacks and Branch Vents

Size of Soil (in.) or Waste Stack	Fixture Units Connected	Diameter of vent required (in.)								
		1½	2	2½	3	4	5	6	8	10
		Maximum developed length of vent (ft.)**								
1½	4	100	†	...	...	...	...	...	...	...
2	8	30	170	†	...	...	...	...	...	...
2½	30	15	70	175	†	...	...	...	...	...
3	97	6	24	89	250	†	...	...	...	...
4	507	*	*	11	78	310	†	...	...	...
5	1445	*	*	*	16	110	380	†	...	...
6	2918	*	*	*	*	34	143	380	†	...
8	6992	*	*	*	*	*	14	73	340	†
10	...	*	*	*	*	*	*	*	*	†

*not permitted.

**A 1½-inch vent may be used for 6 or less fixture units for a developed length of 15 ft. from the fixture to header regardless of developed length limiting the header size.

†Unlimited.

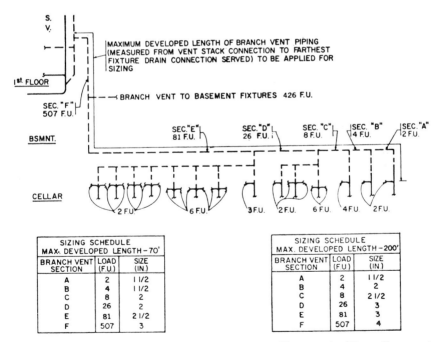

Fig. RS 16-2. Sizing of Branch Vent Piping, Drop Vents to 1st Floor, Basement and Cellar Fixtures.

(c) Connection at base or top.—Main vents.—

(1) At base.—Connect to house drain, soil or waste stack at or below lowest drainage connection.

(2) At top.—Extended undiminished in size through roof, reconnected to a vent header, or to a vent portion of stack a minimum of 6 inches above flood level rim of highest fixture connecting to this soil or waste stack.

(d) Angle of offsets or connections.—

(1) Minimum of 45 degrees from horizontal above highest fixture unless material is of non-scaling type. (Galvanized pipe may be used.)

(2) Minimum of 45 degrees from the horizontal at bottom, unless washout connection provided above offset.

(e) Vent headers.—Such connections to be made at top of stacks. Material to be of non-scaling type. (Galvanized pipe may be used.)

§P109.4   **Vent terminals.—**

(a) Extension above roofs.—

Minimum, 24 inches above roof.

Minimum, 7 ft. above roof if roof is used for other than weather protection.

(b) Size of vent extensions.—

(1) Same size as stack, minimum 4 inches.

(2) Otherwise long increaser required below roof.

(c) Waterproof flashings.—Required for each vent terminal.

(d) Attachments prohibited to vent terminals.—Television aerials, etc.

(e) Location of vent terminal.—

(1) 10 ft., minimum, from any building opening, or 3 ft., minimum, above top of any opening.

(2) Vent extension shall not run through an exterior wall.

(f) Extensions outside building.—No soil, waste or vent line permitted on outside of a building wall. May be installed on penthouses with permission of Commissioner.

§P109.5   **Vent grading and connections.—**

(a) Vent grading.—To drain back to a soil or waste line.

(b) Height above fixtures.—Vent connection to vent stack or stack vent shall be minimum of 6 inches above flood rim of highest fixture.

Branch or relief vents also to be minimum of 6 inches above flood rim of highest fixture served.

See Fig. RS 16-4 for METHODS of compliance.

§P109.6   **Stack venting.—**Permitted for topmost fixture.

§P109.7   **Common vents.—**Also mentioned as DUAL VENTS or UNIT VENTS.

See definitions P100. For example see Fig. RS 16-4 and Diagram 14.

§P109.8   **Fixture vents.—**

(a) Distance of trap from vent.—Maximum, 2 ft. developed length, from vent fitting to trap weir.

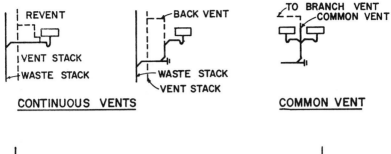

CONTINUOUS VENTS   COMMON VENT

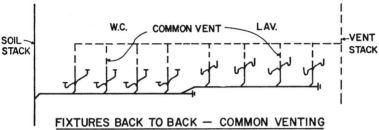

FIXTURES BACK TO BACK — COMMON VENTING

Fig. RS 16-4. Vent Arrangements.

    (b) Vent location.—Not below weir of trap, except water closet or similar fixture.

    (c) Crown venting prohibited.—No vent permitted within 2 pipe diameters of trap weir.

    (d) Floor drain vents.—No vent required when floor drain is within 15 ft. from a vented line. (Cellar floor drains also now on this basis.) See Diagram 26.

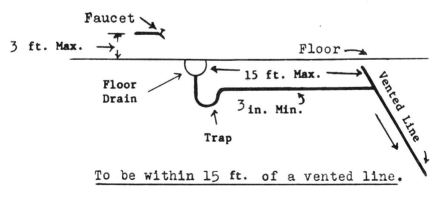

To be within 15 ft. of a vented line.

Floor Drains.—Diagram 26.

§P109.9   **Relief vents.—**

(a) Vertical offsets in building drains.—Where an offset of the horizontal house drain rises vertically over 10 ft., a relief vent to be provided at top of the vertical offset. To be at least 1/2 the diameter of the house drain. To be of sufficient height to prevent the possibility of being used for a soil or waste pipe. See Fig. RS 16-6 for typical installation.

(b) Soil and waste stacks more than 10 stories high.—A yoke relief vent required every 10th story, counting from the top story. Lower end of yoke vent to connect to soil or waste stack through a Y connected below the horizontal branch drain in that story. The upper end to connect to vent stack a minimum of 3 ft. above floor level. See Fig. RS 16-7.

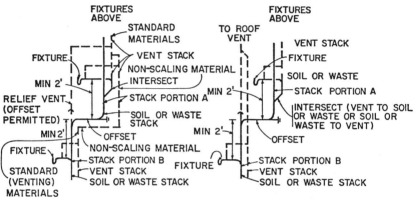

Fig. RS 16-6. Offsets in buildings of five stories or more.

§P109.10   **Suds pressure-zone vents.—**

(a) Where sinks, laundry trays, washing machines, etc., using sudsy detergents are discharged into a soil or waste stack from an upper level which also serves plumbing fixtures in an occupancy unit at a lower level. The discharge and vent piping for the lower fixtures to be arranged to **avoid** connections to suds pressure zones in the drainage and vent system.

If so connected, a SUDS RELIEF VENT to a nonpressure zone to be provided at each suds pressure zone of such connections. The relief vent size to be at least 3/4 the diameter of the piping where the pressure zone occurs, but not less than 2 inches.

(b) Suds pressure zones considered to exist at the following locations in the sanitary drainage and vent systems when fixtures on 2 or more floors receive waste with sudsy detergents. See Fig. RS 16-8 for location of suds pressure zones.

(1) In a soil or waste stack a zone shall be considered to exist in the vertical portion within 40 stack diameters of the base fitting.

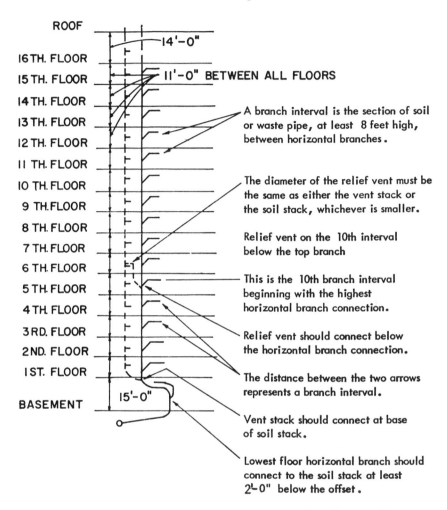

ROOF

16 TH. FLOOR

14'-0"

15 TH. FLOOR — 11'-0" BETWEEN ALL FLOORS

14 TH. FLOOR

13 TH. FLOOR — A branch interval is the section of soil
or waste pipe, at least 8 feet high,
between horizontal branches.

12 TH. FLOOR

11 TH. FLOOR

10 TH. FLOOR — The diameter of the relief vent must be
the same as either the vent stack or
the soil stack, whichever is smaller.

9 TH. FLOOR

8 TH. FLOOR — Relief vent on the 10th interval
below the top branch

7 TH. FLOOR

6 TH. FLOOR — This is the 10th branch interval
beginning with the highest
horizontal branch connection.

5 TH. FLOOR

4 TH. FLOOR

3 RD. FLOOR — Relief vent should connect below
the horizontal branch connection.

2 ND. FLOOR

1 ST. FLOOR — The distance between the two arrows
represents a branch interval.

15'-0"

BASEMENT — Vent stack should connect at base
of soil stack.

Lowest floor horizontal branch should
connect to the soil stack at least
2'-0" below the offset.

Fig. RS 16-7. Relief vents for stack of more than ten branch intervals.

(2) In the horizontal drain at the base of a soil or waste stack a zone shall be considered to exist in the horizontal portion within ten stack diameters of the base fitting. Where a 60-degree or 90-degree fitting is installed in the horizontal drain, a zone shall be considered to exist in the horizontal portion within 40 drain diameters upstream of and 10 drain diameters downstream of the fitting.

(3) In a soil or waste stack offset of 60 degrees or 90 degrees, a zone shall be considered to exist in the vertical portion of the stack within 40 stack diameters of the base fitting for the upper section of the stack. The zone shall be considered to exist in the horizontal offset within 10 stack diameters of such base fitting and within 40 stack diameters of the top fitting for the lower section of the stack.

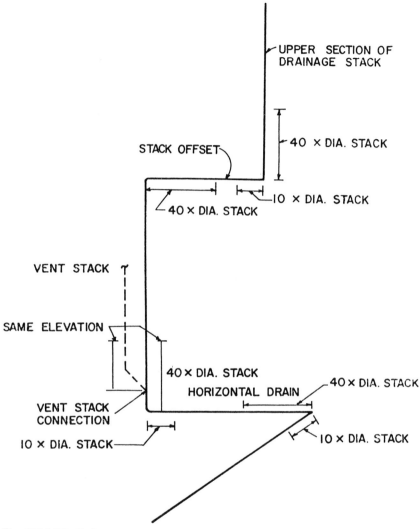

Fig. RS 16-8. Suds pressure zones.

(4) In a vent stack that has its base connected to a suds pressure zone in the sanitary drainage system, a zone shall be considered to exist in the portion of the vent stack extending from its base connection up to the lowest branch vent fitting located above the level of the suds pressure zone in the sanitary drainage system. For typical EXAMPLE see Fig. RS 16-8.

§P109.11   **Permitted combination waste and vent systems.—**
LIMITED for use of floor drains and laboratory sinks.
Permitted to be used with OIL SEPARATOR or ACID WASTE SYSTEMS.
See Fig. RS 16-9.

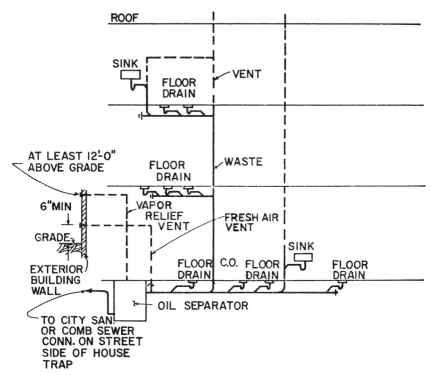

Fig. RS 16-9. Combination waste and vent oil waste drainage.

SECTION P110.0 STORM DRAINAGE PIPING

§P110.1   **Permits.**—

(1) Obtained from Building Department for installation to street sewer.

(2) Obtained from Department of Public Works for street sewer connections. Street sewer connections to be made as provided in Section P108.2 for "Sanitary" sewers.

§P110.2   **Where required.**—Provisions to be made to connect all storm water drainage to a "Storm" sewer or a "Combined" sewer. If no sewer available use method approved by Commissioner.

For one- or two-family dwellings.—Not necessary to connect storm water drainage if it can be drained away from building and not onto sidewalk or adjacent property.

(a) Paved area 25 sq ft or less can be leached into ground.

(b) Area and garage drains to be connected if "Storm" sewer or "Combined" sewer is available.

Permitted by gravity drain, sump, or pump.

(c) Clear water drains, such as air conditioning drips, etc., may connect to storm system in indirect waste manner through trapped funnel or drain.

§P110.3   STORM WATER DRAINAGE TO "SANITARY" SEWER PROHIBITED.

§P110.4   **Size of storm drains and leaders.**—

(a) Building storm drainage sized as per Table RS 16-17.

(b) Storm sewers.—Where more than one building storm drain discharges into a PRIVATE SEWER, minimum of 3 fps velocity required.

(c) Vertical leaders.—To be sized as per Table RS 16-18. Comparing rectangular leaders to circular leaders. Diameter of a 4″ x 3″ rectangular leader considered to equal 1 1/3 to 3-inch circular leader.

(d) Roof gutters.—To be sized as per Table RS 16-19.

(e) Combined drains and sewers.—

(1) Fixture units and square feet of drained area to be converted to equivalent square footage of drained area. For "COMPUTATION," see Table RS 16-20. For "PIPE SIZES," see Table RS 16-17 or Table RS 16-13.

(2) "Sanitary" and "Storm" system COMPUTED up to their point of junction.

(3) "Sanitary" system sized as per fixture unit basis. (See Table RS 16-13.)

(4) "Storm" system sized as per square feet of drained area. (See Table RS 16-17.)

Size of horizontal run from leader to house drain sized as per Table RS 16-17.

(5) Leaders sized as per columns in Table RS 16-18.

(6) After point of junction of "Sanitary" drainage and "Storm" drainage, sizing to be as per Table RS 16-17.

§P110.5   **Values for continuous flow.**—As for pump, air conditioner, etc., each gpm equal to 19 sq. ft. of roof area.

Table RS16-17. Size of Horizontal Storm Drains

Diameter of Drain (in.)	1/8-in. Slope	1/4-in. Slope	1/2-in. Slope
	Maximum Projected Roof Area for Various Slopes of Drains (Sq. ft.)		
2	250	350	500
2½	357	505	714
3	690	930	1,320
4	1,500	2,120	3,000
5	2,700	3,800	5,320
6	4,300	6,100	8,700
8	9,300	13,000	18,400
10	16,600	23,500	33,000
12	26,700	37,500	53,000
15	47,600	67,000	95,000

Table RS16-18. Size of Vertical Leaders

Diameter of Leader or Conductor (in.)	gpm	Maximum Projected Roof Area (sq. ft.)
2	22.6	433
2½	39.6	779
3	66.6	1,278
4	143	2,745
5	261	4,992
6	423	8,121
8	911	17,491
10	1,652	31,718

Table RS16-19. Size of Roof Gutters[a]

Diameter of Gutter[a] (in.)	1/16 in. Slope	1/8 in. Slope	1/4 in. Slope	1/2 in. Slope
	Maximum Projected Roof Area for Gutters of Various Slopes (sq. ft.)			
3	144	192	272	385
4	288	409	575	815
5	500	705	1,000	1,420
6	770	1,090	1,540	2,220
7	1,150	1,560	2,220	3,120
8	1,590	2,250	3,180	4,490
10	3,600	4,080	5,780	8,000

Note.—
[a]Gutters other than semicircular may be used provided they have the same cross-sectional area.

Table RS 16-20. "Fixture Unit-Drainage Square Footage" Equivalent

Drainage Area (sq. ft.)	Fixture Unit Equivalent
180	6
260	10
400	20
490	30
1,000	105
2,000	271
3,000	437
4,000	604
5,000	771
7,500	1,188
10,000	1,500
15,000	2,500
20,000	3,500
28,000	5,500
each additional 3 sq. ft.	1 fixture unit

§P110.6   CONTROLLED FLOW STORM WATER SYSTEM.–Alternate method to P110.4. For complete details see Building Code.

§P110.7   **Traps on storm drains or leaders.**–

(a) Where required.–

(1) Storm drains to a "combined" sewer to be trapped.

(2) Storm drains require no "fresh air inlet."

(3) Intake and exhaust plenum drains, connected to a storm sewer, to be trapped.

(4) One trap may serve more than one drain (within 15 ft.).

Note.–Regarding No. 4, above: See Section P104.17 (e) for somewhat similar statement regarding floor drains.

(b) Where not required.–No traps shall be required for storm water drains that are connected to a building house drain or building house sewer carrying storm water exclusively.

(c) Trap equivalent.–A hooded catch basin located within the street line shall be the equivalent of a building or house trap for the connection to a street combined sewer.

(d) Method of installation.–Individual storm water traps shall be installed on the storm water drain branch serving each conductor, or a single trap shall be installed in the main storm drain just before its connection with the combined building sewer, main drain, or public sewer.

§P110.8   **Leaders or storm water piping.**–

(a) Improper use of storm water piping.–**Not to be used as soil, waste, or vent piping.**

(b) Protection of rainwater conductors.–To be protected by metal guards, be recessed into the wall, or be constructed of pipe.

(c) Method of connection of storm water with sanitary drainage in a "COMBINED SYSTEM." STORM PIPING TO BE CONNECTED AT LEAST 40 DIAMETERS DOWNSTREAM FROM A SOIL STACK. See Diagram 27.

§P110.9   **Roof drain strainers.**–

(a) General use.–To have strainers extending at least 4 inches above roof. Strainer inlet to have at least 1 1/2 times area of pipe.

(b) Flat decks.–Sun decks, etc.–

Roof drain strainers may be flat surface type at least two times area of leader pipe.

§P110.10   **Roof drain flashings required.**–To be watertight.

§P110.11   **Expansion joints required.**–If necessary. See Diagram 28.

§P110.12   **"Sanitary" and "Storm" sewers.**–May be laid in same trench if installed on same property.

§P110.13   **Dry Wells.**–

(a) Dry wells required.–For storm water if no "Combined" or "Storm" sewer in street.

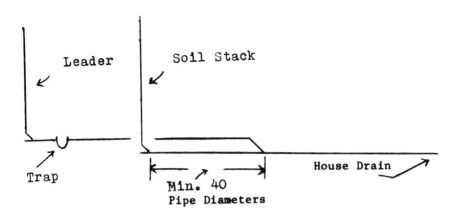

Connection of Storm Water Piping to "Combined House Drain."—Diagram 27. See Section P110.8(c).

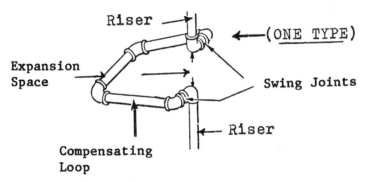

Expansion Joint.—Diagram 28.

(b) Dry wells not required.—For one- and two-family dwellings if:
   (1) Nonporous stratum exists within 8 ft. of grade.
   (2) Also see Section P110.2.
(c) Size of dry well.—See Fig. RS 16-13, and Table RS 16-23. For specific details see Building Code Section P113.9 regarding soil percolation tests.

SECTION P111.0 INDIRECT WASTE PIPING

§P111.1   **Indirect waste connections required.**—
   (a) Where backing up of drainage system would cause:
      (1) Contamination of food, drinks, or food utensils.
      (2) Contamination of surgical and medical equipment.

(b) Food handling devices.—

(1) Waste piping from such devices as refrigerators, food boxes, egg boilers, coffee urns, etc., **MUST** connect to **INDIRECT WASTE.** Culinary and open sinks shall have **DIRECT WASTE** and vent.

(2) Laundry washers and extractors.—

(3) Drains and overflows.—Relief pipes, etc.

(4) Sterilizers.—

(5) Drips or drainage outlets.—Apparatus not classified as plumbing fixtures.

(6) Clear water wastes.—Expansion tanks, etc.

(7) Swimming pools.—See Diagram 29.

(8) Pressure tanks, boilers and relief valves.—Drains to be connected through indirect wastes.

(9) Refrigerators.—

(a) Each indirect waste pipe from a refrigerator or equipment used for storage of food shall discharge into a receptacle through an air break.

(b) No trap permitted ahead of air break.

(c) The maximum developed length of piping between the outlet and the air break shall be 2 ft.

(c) Minimum of 1 inch permitted for air break. See Diagram 1.

§P111.2   **Common indirect wastes.**—Indirect wastes **MAY** be used for bar sinks, soda fountains, drinking fountains, etc., if trapped.

§P111.3   **Venting.**—

(a) No vent required if indirect waste does not exceed 100 ft.

(b) No vent required if indirect wastes for show case refrigerators do not exceed 25 ft.

(c) If vent required.—To be **independent** of drainage system vents.

§P111.4   **Sizing.**—To be sized on fixture unit basis. See Table RS 16-12 and Table RS 16-13. Developed length not to apply.

§P111.5   **Receptors or sumps.**—Waste receptors or sumps serving indirect wastes (such as slop sinks):

(a) Installation.—

(1) Shall not be installed in a toilet room, inaccessible area, or an unventilated area.

(2) Receptor to be shaped to prevent flooding or splashing.

(3) Standpipe receptors for automatic clothes washers.—

(a) To have trap above floor and to be vented. Standpipe to be between 18 inches and 30 inches above trap weir.

(b) May be installed in the grating of a trapped floor drain.

(b) Strainers and baskets.—Receptors (such as slop sinks) to have RE-MOVABLE beehive strainers 4 inches high, minimum.

(c) Domestic or culinary fixtures prohibited as receptors.–(EXCEPTION) in a DWELLING. A dishwasher can connect into a sink waste. See Section P104.11(b).

A clothes washing machine may discharge into a washtub.

§P111.6   **Condensers and sumps.**–Over 150 degree F water pipe or steam pipe drain not permitted to discharge into the drainage system. **Except** 180 degree water from a commercial dishwasher or laundry. Such pipes, except from the dishwasher, to be connected by an indirect waste.

SECTION P112.0 SPECIAL AND MISCELLANEOUS WASTE PIPING

§P112.1   **Industrial wastes.**–Industrial waste permit required from Department of Public Works except as hereinafter provided.

§P112.2   **Chemical wastes.**–

(a) To be **treated** before entering regular drainage system.

(b) Use **independent** sanitary drainage system to a NEUTRALIZING device as per Section P105.0, or a system designed by an architect or engineer, subject to approval of Commissioner or other agency having jurisdiction.

(c) Chemical waste and vent piping to be installed as per Section P102.4(b)(5).

(d) Drainage and vent piping to be sized as per Sections P108.0 and P109.0.

(e) All acid traps to be deep seal.

(f) Acid drainage system on 4 floors or less.–When maximum horizontal branch from stack does not exceed 30 ft., no branch vent is required and the waste stack can serve as a WET VENT. See Fig. RS 16-10 for typical installation.

(g) Acid diluting sump may be located at or beneath fixture. Vent may be treated as a sanitary vent.

(h) Common acid diluting sump to be located at lowest story above house drain. A separate acid dilution sump may be used for fixtures on first floor and below, and the drainage may be pumped into the gravity drainage system. Inlet to sump to have a relief vent 1/2 the diameter of the inlet or a minimum of 2 inches in diameter, whichever is greater. Relief vent to terminate at roof or at acid system vent stack or stack vent.

(i) Each drainage pipe that extends more than 30 ft. from the stack or has more than ten fixture units discharging into it shall be provided with a vent connection from the vent stack or stack vent to a connection in the drain line installed between the last two fixtures on the drain line and each 30 ft. increment. Also, a relief vent shall be installed in the horizontal branch waste within 4 ft. of the stack. See Fig. RS 16-11 for typical installation.

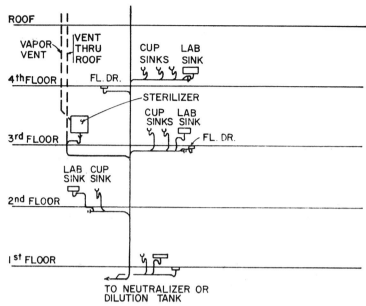

Note.—No venting if each branch to stack has 10 fix. units or less and is less than 30'-0".
If branch is over 30'-0" installation shall be as shown on Fig. RS 16-11.

Fig. RS 16-10. Acid drainage for buildings four stories or less.

(j) Fixtures such as floor drains, receptors receiving the indirect waste
from sterilizers, stills, and drains from other laboratory equipment within
the laboratory area may be connected to the acid drainage system, if the
fixtures, excluding floor drains, are provided with individual vents, and all
of the piping connecting these fixtures of acid resistant material, or when
permitted by the Commissioner, of cast iron.

(k) **Materials** to be as per Sections P102.4(b)(5) and P102.4(c)(3).

§P112.3   **Flammable solvents or oil wastes.**—See Section P105.0 or method
approved by the Department of Public Works. See Fig. RS 16-9 for typical
installation.

§P112.4   **Radioactive wastes.**—As per design of architect or engineer subject
to the approval of the Commissioner and any other agency having jurisdiction.

SECTION P113.0 INDIVIDUAL SEWAGE SYSTEMS

§P113.1   **Information required by applicant.**—Regarding construction of a
PRIVATE sewage system.—Applicant to file with the Department of Buildings a statement obtained from the Department of Public Works, stating
that no sewer is available, and stating the distance to the nearest sewer.

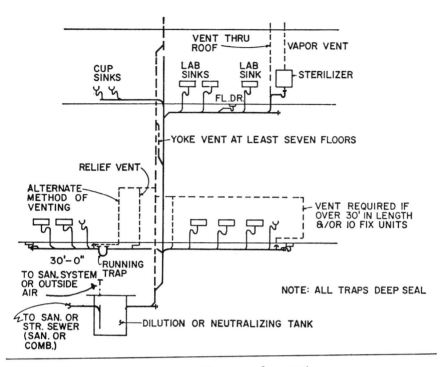

Fig. RS 16-11. Acid drainage for buildings over four stories.

§P113.2   **Individual sewage disposal systems.**—Where no sewer available.

(a) Use a method to be designed by an architect or engineer.

(b) Approval of Commissioner required.

§P113.3   **Individual sewage disposal systems** (For one- and two-family dwellings).—Where no public sewer is available, install a PRIVATE sewage disposal system as per this Code.

§P113.4   **Housing development sewage disposal systems.**—For more than 15 one-family dwellings or a multiple dwelling of 15 or more units.

To be installed as per requirements of the Department of Public Works.

§P113.5   **General requirements.**—METHOD

(a) Install a septic tank with a seepage pit or a disposal field. Septic tanks not to discharge into an open stream.

(b) Storm water or ground water not permitted to discharge into this system.

(c) The use of cesspools is prohibited.

§P113.6   **Location.**—For the minimum distances permitted between components of a sewage system see Table RS 16-21. All parts of the system to be within property line.

**Table RS16-21. Minimum Distances Between Sewage System Components
and Between Components and Incumbrances**

System Components	Bldg. Foundation Wall	Property Line	Disposal Field	Seepage Pits	Water Service	Drywell
Septic Tanks	5 ft.	...	5 ft.	5 ft.	...	...
Disposal Field	5 ft (no Bsmts.) 10 ft. (with Bsmts.)	5 ft.	...	...	10 ft.	20 ft.
Seepage Pits	15 ft.	... 10 ft.*	... ...	... ...	... 10 ft.	... 20 ft.
Drywells	10 ft.	10 ft.*	20 ft.	20 ft.	...	...

Note.—
*The seepage pit may be located next to the property line upon written approval of the Commissioner.

§P113.7   **Septic tanks.**—CONCRETE or METAL construction.
   (1) For **DETAILS of a septic tank** see Fig. RS 16-12.
   (2) For **CAPACITY of a septic tank** see Table RS 16-22.
   (3) For specific construction details see Building Code.

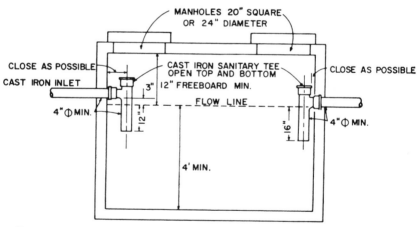

*Note.—*In lieu of the cast iron tees, concrete baffles may be installed. The baffles shall be 4 inches to 6 inches from the inlet and outlet ends of the tank and extend a distance of approximately 6 inches above the flow line. The baffle shall extend 12 inches below the flow line on the inlet end, and 16 inches below the flow line on the outlet end.

Fig. RS 16-12. Details of septic tank.

Table RS16-22. Minimum Capacity of Septic Tanks

Type of Dwelling	Number of Bedrooms	Minimum Capacity of Tank to Flow Line, Including Sludge Accumulation (gal.)
1 Family	2	750
1 Family	3	900
1 Family	4	1,050
1 Family	5	1,200
1 Family	6 or more	See P113.7(c)
2 Family	4	1,350
2 Family	5	1,500
2 Family	6	1,800
2 Family	7	2,000
2 Family	8	2,160
	9 or more	See P113.7(c)

§P113.8 **Distribution box.**—Installed between septic tank and disposal field. For specific construction details see Building Code.

§P113.9 **Soil percolation tests.**—Percolation rate shall be used with Table RS 16-23, to determine the effective absorptive area of a trench or seepage pit. For specific details see Building Code.

§P113.10 **Seepage pits.**—

(a) Capacity.—The liquid capacity (volume below inlet line) of seepage pits shall be at least equal to that of the septic tank, as prescribed in Table RS16-22. In addition, sufficient wall area shall be provided to permit the liquid wastes to leach into the soil without overflowing. Effective absorption area; i.e., the wall area at the outer circumference of the annular stone shall be in accordance with Table RS16-23.

(b) Construction.—The seepage pit shall be structurally sound. The piping from the septic tank to the pit shall have tight joints. The general construction arrangement shall be in accordance with Fig. RS 16-13.

(c) Water table.—No seepage pit shall extend into the water table. Where ground water is encountered, the bottom of the pit shall be raised at least 2 ft. above the water table by the use of clean coarse sand. In locations of a tidal water table, the seepage-pit bottom may be at the elevation of mean high water prevailing in the area.

§P113.11 **Subsurface disposal field.**—

(a) Installations from the building shall be in the following order: Septic tank, Distribution box, Disposal field in open, shaded areas.

(1) To contain at least 2 lateral lines.

(2) Any line to be at least 20 ft. from the center line of any tree trunk.

Table RS16-23. Design Data for Absorptive Capacity of
Subsurface Disposal Field and Seepage Pits

Percolation Rate Percolation Test rate in minutes for water to fall 1 in.	Effluent Allowance Rate of Septic Tank in gal. per sq. ft. of effective absorptive area per day	
	Disposal Field Trenches (bottom of trenches)	Seepage Pits (wall area)
2 or less	3.2	4.3
5	2.4	3.2
10	1.7	2.3
30	0.8	1.1
60 (not recommended)	0.4	0.6
Over 60 (not suitable)	Obtain special approval of the Commissioner. Use special design by an architect or engineer, subject to the approval of the Commissioner.	

Note.—Volume of sewage to be disposed of should be equal to the 24-hr. sewage flow.
No portion of the field shall be installed under any pavement or any area where there
will be vehicular traffic or parking.

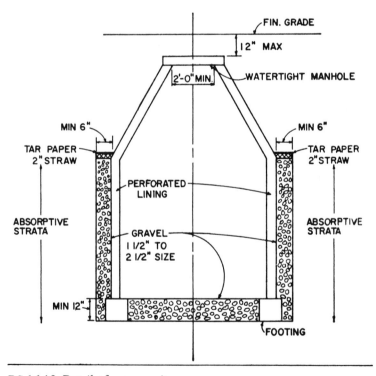

Fig. RS 16-13. Detail of seepage pit.

(b) Construction.—Open joint pipe, cast iron, clay, perforated pipe, etc. Open jointed pipe to have top half covered with asphalt-treated paper, or to be protected while pipe is being covered.

(c) Filter material.—For specific details see Building Code.

(d) Size of trench area for disposal field.—To be determined by soil percolation tests and Table RS 16-23.

(e) Distance requirements.—See Table RS 16-24.

§P113.12   Maintenance.—Information regarding location of septic tank to be available at premises.

Table RS 16-24. Limiting Dimensions of Disposal Field Components

Limit	Components
Individual lines, maximum length	100 ft.
Individual lines, lengths	All of equal length
Field tile, minimum diameter	4 in.
Field tile, maximum slope	6 in. per 100-ft. length
Field tile, open joint, minimum space in joint	¼ in.
Trench or bed bottom, minimum depth	18 in.
Trench or bed bottom, average depth	not more than 30 in.
Trench or bed bottom, minimum above ground water	2 ft.
Trench bottom, minimum width (percolation rate of 2 minutes or less)	18 in.
Trench bottom, minimum width (percolation rate of 5 to 10 minutes)	24 in.
Trench bottom, maximum width for other more impervious soils	30 in.
Trench or bed, minimum separation between	3 times trench width but not less than 6 ft.

SECTION P114.0   HOSPITAL AND INSTITUTIONAL PLUMBING

§P114.1   General.—Requirements as per this Code.

§P114.2   Definitions for special hospital fixtures and equipment.—

Aspirator.—A suction equipment used in hospitals. See Section P107.13.

Autopsy table.—Used for post-mortem examination of a body. See Section P107.13.

Bedpan hopper.—Used for flushing bedpans (Clinic sinks). See Section P114.3(a) and (b).

Bedpan steamer.—A fixture used for sanitizing bedpans or urinal bottles.

Bedpan washer.—Flushes bedpan contents into the sanitary drainage system.

Bedpan washer device.—Used for cleaning bedpans. It is supplied with hot and/or cold water, located adjacent to a water closet or clinic sink or in the discharge piping of a flush valve.

Bedpan washer vent.—A LOCAL VENT. See Diagram 9.

Clinic sink.—(See bedpan hopper.)

Sterilizer.—Used for boiling instruments and other equipment for purpose of disinfection. See Section P107.13 for requirements.

Still.—A device used for distilling liquids.

§P114.3 **Requirements for special hospital fixtures and equipment.**—Bedpan hoppers (clinic sinks), bedpan washers, etc., subject to the following requirements:

(a) Bedpan hoppers (clinic sinks).—

(1) To contain an integral trap and flushing characteristics of a water closet.

(2) Flushing rim (to be self cleansing).

(b) Use of clinic sink.—**Prohibited** for use as a janitor's sink and vice versa.

(c) Ice-manufacturing machine or device for storage of ice.—**Shall be** in a clean utility room, floor pantry, diet kitchen or other similar location, not near a clinic sink, bedpan washer, etc.

(d) Sterilizers.—

(1) Not to be descaled or chemically treated while connected to the water supply or drainage system.

(2) New pressure type sterilizers to conform to ASME Boiler and Pressure Vessel Code, 1962, Section VIII.

(3) Piping to be accessible.

(a) Steam supply.—The condensate drainage from the steam supply shall be discharged by gravity.

(b) Condenser.—Pressure sterilizers to have means of condensing exhaust steam vapors.

(c) Gas fired equipment.—Gas-fired equipment with water supply or drainage connections, to comply with rules of the Building Code.

§P114.4 **Plumbing in mental hospitals.**—

(a) No traps or pipes to be exposed.

(b) Fixtures shall be securely bolted **through** wall.

§P114.5 **Number of plumbing fixtures.**—The minimum number of fixtures for HOSPITALS AND INSTITUTIONS shall be as per Table RS 16-25.

§P114.6 **Drainage and venting.**—

(a) Ice storage-chest drains.—

(1) To discharge into an indirect waste receptor.

(2) Each drain to discharge through an air break above the receptor.

(3) End of drain to be covered with a removable screen of at least 10 mesh per inch or with a flap valve.

(b) Bedpan washers and clinic sinks.—Shall have a local vent.

§P114.7 **Sterilizer wastes.**—

(a) Indirect wastes required.—Each sterilizer shall be provided with an individual and separate indirect waste, and with an air break having a

Table RS16-25. Minimum Number of Fixtures for Hospitals and Institutions

Type of Building Occupancy	Type of Fixtures					
	Water Closets	Urinals	Lavatories	Bathtubs or Showers	Drinking Fountains	Other Fixtures
Institutional–Other than hospitals or penal institutions (on each occupied story)	1 for each 25 men 1 for each 20 women	1 for each 50 men	1 for each 20 persons	1 for each 10 persons	1 for each 50 persons	
Hospitals–general.	In accordance with the Hospital Code of the City of New York					
Hospital–employees. 2d Public Facilities			(See Table RS16-5)			
Institutional–prisoners	1 in each cell 1 in each exercise room	1 in each exercise room	1 in each cell 1 in each exercise room	1 in each cell block floor	1 on each cell block floor 1 in each exercise area	
Institutional–employees and Public Facilities			(See Table RS16-5)			1 slop sink per floor
Nursing homes	In accordance with the Nursing-Home Code of the City of New York					

diameter at least twice that of the waste tailpiece. The upper rim of the receptor, funnel, or basket type fitting shall be at least 2 inches below the vessel or the piping, whichever is lower.

Except as provided in (b), below, a "P" trap shall be installed on the discharge side of, and immediately below the waste connection serving each sterilizer.

(b) Floor drain required.—In all rooms containing the recessed or concealed portions of sterilizers, the entire floor area shall be drained and at least one floor drain shall be installed. The floor drain waste and trap shall have a minimum diameter of 3 inches. It shall receive the drainage from at least one sterilizer to assure maintenance of the floor drain trap seal. No individual sterilizer waste trap shall be required on this type of installation.

(c) Bedpan steamers, additional trap required.—A trap with a minimum seal of 3 inches shall be provided in a bedpan steam drain located between the fixture and the indirect waste connection.

(d) Pressure sterilizer.—For specific details see Building Code.

(e) Exhaust condenser drains.—Shall be installed with an indirect waste connection.

(f) Water sterilizer.—All water sterilizer drains, including tank, valve, condenser, filter and cooling, shall be installed with an indirect waste connection.

(g) Pressure-type instrument washer-sterilizer drain.—Shall be installed with an indirect waste connection.

§P114.8   **Vapor vents.**—

(a) Vent material.—Shall be as required in Section P102.4 (Galvanized pipe may be used.).

(b) Vent connections prohibited.—Not permitted to connect to sanitary drainage and vent system. Only one type of apparatus shall be served by a given type vent.

(c) Bedpan vents and stacks.—

(1) Bedpan washers.—

(a) Shall be at least 2-inch diameter pipe.

(b) Shall vent to outer atmosphere above roof.

(c) May drip into fixture served.

(2) Multiple installations.—Where bedpan washers are located above each other, a bedpan vent stack is permitted. See Table RS 16-26 for vent sizing.

(3) Trap required.—The bottom of the bedpan vent stack, except when serving only one bedpan washer, shall be drained by means of a trapped waste connection discharging indirectly into the plumbing sanitary drainage system. The trap and waste shall be at least 2 inches in size.

Table RS16-26. Stack Sizes for Bedpan Steamers and Boiling Type
Sterilizers and Number of Connections Permitted

Stack Size (in.)	Connection Size (in.)		
	1½		2
	No. of Connections Permitted		
1½	1	or	0
2	2	or	1
2	1	and	1
3	4	or	2
3	2	and	2
4	8	or	4
4	4	and	4

(4) Trap seal maintenance.—A water supply of at least ¼-inch tubing shall be taken from the flush supply of each bedpan washer on the discharge or fixture side of the vacuum breaker, trapped to form at least a 3-inch seal, and connected to the local vent on each floor. The water supply shall be so installed as to provide a supply of water to the local vent stack for cleansing and drain trap seal maintenance each time a bedpan washer is flushed.

(d) Pressure sterilizer vent and stacks.—In multiple installations, vent connections to stack to be made by inverted type fittings and this vent stack to be drained to lowest sterilizer funnel or basket-type waste fitting or receptor.

§P114.9   **Sizing of sterilizer vent stacks.**—

(a) Bedpan steamers.—The minimum diameter of a sterilizer vent serving a bedpan steamer shall be 1½ inch. Multiple installations shall be sized according to Table RS 16-26.

(b) Boiler type sterilizer.—The minimum diameter of a sterilizer vent stack shall be 2 inches when serving a utensil sterilizer, and 1½ inch when serving an instrument sterilizer. Combinations of boiling type sterilizer vent connections shall be based on Table RS 16-26.

(c) Pressure sterilizers.—The minimum diameter of sterilizer vent stacks or the vertical stack vent from a single unit shall be 2 inches minimum. Stacks serving combinations or pressure sterilizer exhaust connections shall be sized according to Table RS 16-27.

(d) Pressure type instrument washer-sterilizer.—The minimum diameter of a sterilizer vent stack serving an instrument washer-sterilizer shall be 2 inches.

(e) Roof penetration.—Vent shall be increased in size and extended through the roof in accordance with sanitary venting requirements.

**Table RS16-27. Stack Sizes for Pressure Sterilizers and
Number of Connections Permitted**

Stack Size (in.)	Connection Size (in.)						
	¾		1		1¼		1½
	No. of Connections Permitted						
1½	3	or	2	or	1		
1½	2	and	1				
2	6	or	3	or	2	or	1
2	3	and	2				
2	2	and	1	and	1		
2	1	and	1	and			1
3	15	or	1	or	5	or	3
3			1	and	2	and	2
3	1	and	5	and			1

§P114.10   **Water supply.—**

(a) Services.—Hospitals to have at least two water service connections. If more than one street main is available, connection to be made to the different mains.

(b) Water supply protection.—To meet all requirements of **Section P107.0** and **Table RS 16-28.**

Table RS16-28. Fixture Water Supply Protection[a]

Fixtures	Type of Protection	Remarks
Aspirators	Separate water system	...
Bedpan		
Washers	Vacuum breaker	
Washer hose	Vacuum breaker	Locate 5 ft. above floor
Boiler type sterilizer	Air gap	Not less than twice the effective opening of the water supply
Exhaust condenser	Vacuum breaker	...
Pressure type instrument washer-sterilizer	Vacuum breaker	...
Pressure type sterilizer	Vacuum breaker	...

Note.—[a] Where vacuum breakers are used, they shall be installed after the last control valve. See Section P107.20 for requirements for other fixtures.

(c) Hot water supply protection.—Hot water supply to patients' showers, therapeutic equipment, and continuous baths shall be provided with control valves automatically regulating the temperature of the water supply to the fixture. The valve shall fail in a closed position when the tempered water supply to the fixture exceeds 110 degrees F.

§P114.11   **Vacuum systems.**—

(a) Aspirators, water.—The use of water aspirators is prohibited.

(b) Bottle systems.—Vacuum systems intended for collecting, removing and/or disposing of blood, pus, and/or other fluids shall be protected by bottles (furnished as secondary equipment) installed near the outlet. Each vacuum outlet station shall be equipped so as to prevent fluids other than air from entering the vacuum piping systems.

(c) Central system equipment.—The collecting and/or control tanks in central systems shall be provided with drains for cleaning the tanks. The exhausts from vacuum pumps used in connection with a vacuum system shall discharge separately to the outdoor air above the roof or at such other locations as may be permitted by the Commissioner. The exhaust discharge shall, in no case, be located so as to cause a hazard to public safety, health or welfare.

§P114.12   **Oxygen and nitrous oxide systems.**—For specific details see Building Code. The alarms for the system shall comply with the requirements of the Fire Department.

SECTION P115.0 GAS PIPING

§P115.1   **General requirements for gas piping.**—

(a) Gas service and distribution piping

(1) Shall have tight joints

(2) Piping system and appliance installation as per this Code

(3) System tested as per this Code (See Section C26-1606.4[d]).

§P115.2   **Gas service piping connections.**—

(a) Fittings.—

(1) Approved lubricated stopcock installed in accessible position.

(2) Stopcock to be installed within 2 ft. of point of entry of building, or at a location permitted by the Commissioner.

(3) Install stopcock on street side of gas meter; or regulator if any.

(4) Pipe through wall to have sleeve with both ends sealed to prevent entry of water. Sleeve to extend at least 4 inches on outside wall and one inch on inside wall.

(5) If gas line enters through floor slab, sleeve shall be welded to gas piping at both ends, to prevent entry of water or gas.

(b) In high pressure gas area, Utility Company to inspect shut-off stopcock annually.

(c) No gas line, meter, or regulator to be installed within 10 ft. of a stairway except with a wall between.

§P115.3   **Gas regulator and gas regulator vent outlets.**—A gas service line entering a building with over 1/2-psi pressure, to have a pressure reducing regulator to reduce pressure to 1/2 psi on street side of gas meter. EXCEPTION permitted for commercial purposes up to 3 psi, but any higher pressures require approval of Commissioner. **A marked** gas vent to be installed from pressure-reducing regulator to the **outer air.** Gas vent not to be located under any window or opening in building.

FOR AMENDED RULING regarding Sections P115.2 and P115.3 see DE-PARTMENT OF BUILDINGS Directive No. 14, 1970.

The City of New York
HOUSING AND DEVELOPMENT ADMINISTRATION
Department of Buildings

Directive No. 14 /1970

To: Borough Superintendents   Date: April 13, 1970

From: Thomas V. Burke, Director of Operations

Subject: Gas Piping, Shut-off Valves, Pressure Regulators
Sections P115.2 and P115.3 of Reference Standard 16

Where high pressure gas is brought into a building, it is required to be reduced to a pressure of 1/2 lb. p.s.i. or less, within the building, except where higher pressures are specifically authorized under section P115.3. Piping, fixtures, supports and protection shall be as follows:

1. It is required by section P115.2, that the shut-off valve be placed immediately inside of the building at the point where the gas service enters. The valves shall be placed as close to the wall as possible.

2. The gas pressure regulator shall be placed close to the shut-off valve, with a maximum of approximately two feet of length of pipe between the valve and the regulator, and shall be vented directly to the exterior of the building.

3. The gas meter and distribution piping must be placed on the house side of the pressure regulator.

4. Piping containing gas, with a pressure exceeding 1/2 lb. p.s.i., and the pressure regulator, shall be protected from accidental impact, by an enclosure braced to the wall or by other means, with access to the shut-off valve, and adequate venting if enclosed.

5. When the structure is erected on fill or on piles, provisions is to be made to preclude possible damage and leak of the high pressure gas service piping.

6. All other pertinent provisions of law shall be complied with.

TVB:IEM:ap   *Thomas V. Burke*
cc: Commissioner O'Neill   Thomas V. Burke
     Dep. Commissioner Ferro   Director of Operations
     Ass't. Commissioner Padavan
     Executive Staff
     Brooklyn Union Gas Company
     Con Edison

§P115.4   **Outside gas cut-off.—**

(a) To be installed in the gas service pipe outside the building when the pressure exceeds 1/2 psi and where required by the New York State Public Service Commission Code, Rules and Regulations, Part 255.

(b) To have a shut-off valve accessible under an iron cover within 100 ft. of the building.

(c) Shut-off valve to be readily operated with a portable key or rod.

§P115.5   **Gas meter location.—**

(a) Location in one-family dwelling.—

(1) At point of entrance, in basement unless otherwise permitted by Commissioner

(2) In a dry, safe place

(3) Protected from extreme cold or heat

(4) Properly ventilated

(5) Accessible for reading and inspection

(6) Outside meter installation permitted if utility company certifies use of dry-gas distribution.

(b) Location in a multiple dwelling.—

(1) Except for a replacement, a gas meter shall not be installed in a boiler room, a stair hall, or a public hall.

(2) Additional gas meter may be installed in boiler room next to existing gas meters. Additional gas meter to be used for the gas heating boiler or for a gas hot water heater being supplied.

(3) Such additional gas meter may be installed, providing space heaters and hot water appliances in the dwelling units are eliminated.

§P115.6   **Gas piping materials and fittings permitted.—**

(a) Piping materials and piping joints.—All materials used in gas piping systems shall be in accordance with USASI Z21.30-1964, installation of gas appliances and gas piping, subject to the following modifications. This booklet of the USASI (United States of America Standards Institute), formerly American National Standards Institute, is sponsored by AGA (American Gas Association, Inc.).

(b) Installed fittings.—

(1) Fittings hereafter installed shall be made of malleable iron, steel or brass; screwed, welded, or flanged type with approved gasket. **(NO CAST IRON FITTINGS OR BUSHINGS PERMITTED.)**

(2) Ground joint unions or approved type compression couplings may be used from service stopcock to meter.

(3) Ground joint unions permitted between stopcock and appliance. Gasket unions and running threads not permitted.

(4) Compression couplings acceptable to Utility Company may be used on buried piping outside of building.

(5) Installation of cast iron gas piping permitted outside underground.

(6) Used gas pipe, fittings, etc., shall not be reused.

(7) Stopcocks, regulators, controls, etc., to be approved type.

§P115.7   **Installation of gas piping.—**

(a) Installation of gas piping.—Shall be in accordance with the rules of USASI Z21.30-1964, subject to the following modifications:

(1) Piping underground beneath buildings.—Venting shall not be required if casing is welded to pipes on both ends.

(2) Gas pipe shall not be bent. Gas pipes may be bent by a Utility (Gas) Company under the jurisdiction of the Public Service Commission.

(3) Branches from risers shall have a minimum of a 2-elbow swing.

(4) Branch outlet pipes shall be taken from the top or sides of the horizontal lines and not from the bottom.

(5) The gas piping and gas service shall not be used for an electrical ground.

(b) Outside gas piping.—

(1) Outside gas piping shall be minimum of 2 ft. underground unless approved by Commissioner and adequately protected, or certified by the utility company to be DRY gas.

(2) Gas pipe laid in concrete to be coated with preservative paint.

(3) Gas pipe laid underground to be protected from corrosion.

(c) Concealed piping.—As defined in Section 2.8 of USASI Z21.30-1964, concealed piping shall not include piping installed in pipe shafts. When piping is installed in a shaft, the shaft shall have a fire protective rating as prescribed in the requirements for fire protection construction of the Building Code.

§P115.8   **Gas piping sizes.—**Pipe sizes shall be in accordance with USASI Z21.30-1964, subject to modifications of this Code.

Individual outlets to gas ranges shall not be less than 3/4 inch.

FOR GAS SERVICE PIPING.—See Section C26-1600.1

FOR GAS TESTS.—See Section C26-1606.4(d)

SECTION P116.0   SWIMMING POOLS AND DISPLAY POOLS OR FOUNTAINS

Also see Section C26-714.0.

Also see Section C26-1604.0.

Also see Section P111.1(b)(7) Indirect wastes.

§P116.1   **Swimming pools.—**

(a) General requirements.—To be designed, installed and maintained as per rules of the Building Code.

(b) Prohibited pools.—Fill and draw pools.

(c) Toilet and shower facilities.—Shall be convenient and adequate. For specific details see Building Code.

(d) Drainage.—

(1) At least one drain at low end of pool.

(2) Drain, to empty pool within 8 hours.

(3) Anti-vortex device required.—Open area of grating shall be at least 4 times area of drain pipe.

(4) Drains required within every 30 ft., maximum 15 ft. from the side walls.

(5) Overflow gutters to drain to recirculating line.

(6) 2-inch minimum size return piping required. Drain grating to be sized at least 1 1/2 times area of outlet pipe.

(7) For further specific details see Building Code.

(e) Inlets.—Shall be sized and spaced for uniform circulation.

(f) Recirculation and filtration.—For specific details see Building Code.

(g) Hair and lint catchers.—Shall be accessible for cleaning.

(h) Disinfection.—An effective means of disinfection shall be introduced by mechanical means capable of providing at least 8 ppm chlorine at the turnover rate of the pool. Use chlorine or calcium hypochlorite. Ammonia not permitted. Liquefied chlorine may be used when permitted by the Commissioner.

(i) Heating.—No direct steam heating or electric elements permitted.

(j) Make-up water.—Shall be supplied through an air gap.

(k) Water standards and quality.—Water to be supplied from:

(1) Public water supply system, or source approved by the Department of Health.

(2) Water treatment to comply with bacteria test.

(3) Amount of free chlorine in the water at 60 degrees F or less, shall be at least 0.4 ppm; dechlorinated water shall have a pH value in the range of 7.2 to 8.2.

(4) Pool areas to be clean, and water to be clear and clean.

(5) Pool water to be tested in accordance with the rules of the American Public Health Association, American Water Works Association, and Federation of Sewage and Industrial Waste Associations. Water samples to be examined by the Department of Health for maintenance of operating permit.

(l) Pipe identification colors.—

Potable water pipe—green
Recirculation water pipe—light blue
Backwash and wash-water pipe—gray
Chlorine pipe—yellow
Well-water pipe—red

FOR ADDITIONAL P116.1 DETAILS SEE BUILDING CODE. See Diagram 29.

§P116.2   **Display pools and fountains.—**

(a) **No** direct or submerged water connection permitted.

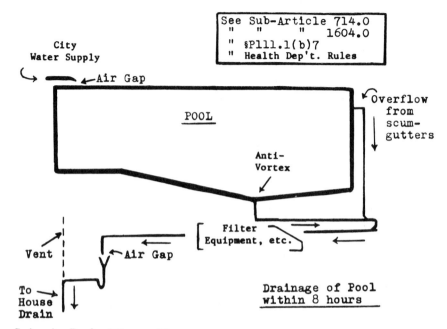

City
Water Supply

See Sub-Article 714.0
  "   "   "   1604.0
  " §P111.1(b)7
  " Health Dep't. Rules

Air Gap

POOL

Overflow
from
scum-
gutters

Anti-
Vortex

Vent

Air Gap

Filter
Equipment, etc.

To
House
Drain

Drainage of Pool
within 8 hours

Swimming Pools.—Diagram 29.

  (b) Drainage
    (1) Drain connections to be provided.
    (2) Circulating or fountain pumps may dispose of waste water to the Sanitary, Storm, or Combined Sewer.
  (c) Recirculation required.—For over 2,000 gallons waste per day.
  (d) Treatment.—The water shall be chemically treated for odor, mosquito breeding, health hazards, etc., or periodically drained, provided water waste does not exceed the amount specified in (c) above.

INDEX
REFERENCE STANDARD RS-16
All references are to Section Numbers

DEPARTMENT OF WATER SUPPLY, GAS AND ELECTRICITY–
RULES AND REGULATIONS

Established by the Acting Commissioner of Water Supply, Gas and Electricity on May 20, 1966, and amended to and including July 11, 1966 (Rule 177D), in conformity with paragraph 3, section 734, Chapter 30 of the New York City Charter and filed with the City Clerk on May 24, 1966 and July 11, 1966, respectively.

PERMITS

General   100. Subject to the provisions of these regulations, permits will
Permits   be issued in the borough offices of the Department of Water Sup-
ply, Gas and Electricity, for the following purposes, upon the receipt of proper applications and satisfactory proof that the applicant has complied with all provisions of the Workmen's Compensation Law.

Air Conditioning Apparatus, Water Cooled
Building Purposes, Regular
Building Purposes, Power Boilers
Building Purposes, Extra, Miscellaneous
Demolition
*Electrical Tap Indicator, Use of
Hydrant, Use of
*Hydrant, Flow or Pressure Test
*Hose Bib, Outside
*Hose, Use of Unmetered
*Hose, Use of Metered
Meter Disconnect for Repair or Change of Piping
Meter, Setting, New or Additional
Refrigeration—Water Cooled
Service Pipe, Installation or Repair
Shipping, Steam Purposes
Shipping, Water Boats
Shipping, Extras
Thawing Service Pipes
Taps and Plugs

*Workmen's Compensation not required.

All work under a permit shall be performed by the permittee, and/or persons directly employed and supervised by the permittee, and shall be subject to the conditions as stated in Section 5 of Rules and Regulations fixing uniform annual charges.

Applications   101. An application for a supply of water shall state the pur-
pose for which it is required, together with name and address of owner of property. Information furnished shall be in affidavit form if so required. No water shall be furnished except to the premises for which application was duly made and permit authorized.

Permits; To Whom Issued. 102. Permits involving plumbing work will be issued only to licensed and bonded plumbers who are duly registered annually in the office of the Department of Buildings, and in the Bureau of Water Register in the boroughs in which the work is to be performed, and to plumbers in the employ of Municipal, State or Federal Governments.

Meter repair permits may be issued to authorized meter repair companies for the repair on the premises of cold water meters 3-inch in size and larger.

102A. Any work done without a permit as required by this Department is a direct violation and must be corrected, as specified by this Department, under a permit.

Licensed Plumbers, Penalties 103. Licensed Plumbers guilty of violating any of the rules and regulations herein established shall be prohibited from securing further permits from this Department, and where wilful violations warrant, the Commissioner may prefer charges to the Department of Health for the revocation of the Violator's Master Plumber's License.

103A. Authorized meter repair companies guilty of violating any of the rules and regulations herein, will be suspended. Where wilful violations warrant, the Commissioner may cancel their authorization.

Approval by Department of Highways 104. Permits from this Department for work requiring the opening of a street may be issued only upon the presentation of a permit from the Department of Highways, or the agency having jurisdiction authorizing such opening.

Building Purpose Charges to be Prepaid 105. A permit for a tap or service pipe for unmetered water that is to be used in the erection of a new, or the alteration of an existing building, will be issued only on prepayment of all building purpose charges for water to be used.

Return of Permits 106. Within twenty-four hours or not later than the next business day following the completion of any work for which a meter permit has been issued, the permit, carrying a certification of the date of completion of the work, shall be returned to the borough office of the Bureau of Water Register.

Permits at Job Location 107. All permits for the use of water on construction work shall be kept in an accessible location on the premises or job.

Emergency Repairs 108. A licensed plumber may render emergency assistance in cases where an accident to a service or meter involves damage or leakage of water supply, but he shall obtain all necessary regular permits as soon as possible. Where it is necessary to open a street to render such assistance, the plumber shall obtain an emergency permit from the local Police Precinct Commander or his authorized representative.

TAPS TO CITY WATER MAINS

Separate Supply. 109. A separate tap and service shall be installed for each building located on a street in which there is a City water main. No consumer will be allowed to supply water to other persons or premises, except in a project where more than one building under a single ownership is supplied from a common house tank or booster system located in or on one of the buildings. The siamesing of taps or services on the inlet side of the main control valve is prohibited. A service line connected to the City main by a three-way or by any means other than a corporation stop or wet connection shall be controlled by a gate valve placed in the service line within two feet of the point of connection to the main.

Connections to City Mains. 110. Corporation stops, wet connections or other connections to a City main shall be inserted or installed only by department employees.

For mains 4 inches or less in diameter direct corporation stop connections shall not exceed one (1) inch in diameter; a 1½-inch corporation stop connection shall be made through a tapping saddle, as directed by the Department. The tapping saddle is to be provided and set by the plumber.

A 2 or 3 inch connection shall be made by a wet connection.

For 6 inch mains, direct corporation stop connections shall not exceed 1½ inches in diameter; 2 inch and larger connections to this size main shall be wet connections.

For mains larger than 6 inches in diameter, direct corporation stop connections shall not exceed 2 inches in diameter; all larger connections shall be wet connections.

Tapping saddles shall be provided by the plumber whenever in the opinion of the Department the wall thicknesses of a pipe to be tapped is not sufficient to securely hold the corporation stop.

Spacing of Corporation Stops and Wet Connections.   111. No corporation stop or wet connections may be inserted on a special casting or within 24 inches of a hub, special castings, hydrant branch, dead end, etc. The minimum spacing interval for corporation stops and wet connections shall be 18 inches for ¾ and 1-inch corporation stops, and 24 inches for 1½ and 2-inch corporation stops and wet connections. No corporation stop or wet connection shall be installed below the horizontal diameter of the City main.

Location of Taps.   112. No tap will be inserted unless the location of the excavation agrees with that shown on the permit. All old taps shall be plugged or destroyed at or before the time of installation of the new tap. The tap shall be inserted in front of the building to be supplied with water, and no tap shall be located in front of a driveway or proposed driveway except when approved by the Department for one and two-family houses.

Charges for Corporation Stops, Plugs and Wet Connections.   113. The charges for a corporation stop, a plug or a wet connection will be for furnishing, delivering and inserting the corporation stop or plug; for furnishing and setting the wet connection sleeve and valve complete and ready for connection to the service pipe. These charges will be fixed by the Commissioner and will be subject, without notice, to such revision as may be required by changes in the costs of labor and materials.

Destruction of Abandoned Corporation Stops and Wet Connections.   114. All driven corporation stops, when abandoned, shall be removed and replaced by screw plugs, unless otherwise authorized by the Bureau of Water Supply. All wet connections and screw corporation stops, when abandoned, shall be destroyed in place and all exposed portions of the service pipes shall be cut and removed. Where a corporation stop or wet connection is destroyed and the connecting service pipe is one equipped with a curb valve and box, the curb box must be removed.

Plugs.   115. If an excavation that is made under a permit covering the removal or destruction of a single tap reveals that the service pipe is supplied by two or more taps, the plumber making the excavation shall be held responsible for the plugging or destruction of the additional taps. The Department will make available to the licensed plumber its records relative to the location of any tap to be plugged or destroyed, but does not guarantee the correctness of these records. The responsibility for locating the tap rests solely with the licensed plumber obtaining the permit.

Method of Destroying Wet Connections and Corporation Stops.   116. All labor and materials necessary to destroy a wet connection shall be furnished by the owner's plumber. The valve shall be closed, stuffing box gland thoroughly tightened, the valve stem cut off flush with stuffing box gland, and service pipe disconnected and plug inserted in outlet end of the valve. Where conditions require it, the plug and valve shall be anchored to the main as directed by the Department. A screw corporation stop shall be destroyed by removing a diagonal portion of the corporation stop thread. A driven corporation stop shall be removed and replaced by a screw plug unless otherwise authorized by the Bureau of Water Supply.

Method of Abandoning Three-way Connection.

117. Three-way connections to be abandoned shall have all piping disconnected and removed from the branch hub of three-way and a plug caulked into such hub, the plug then being properly anchored to the main as directed by the Department. All work shall be done by a licensed plumber. The cost of shutting the main will be charged to the plumber.

Use of Electrical Indicator for Tap Location.

118. Upon application and payment of $15.00 in advance the Department will endeavor to locate a tap by use of an electrical indicator. If the tap is not found within three feet of the location as determined by the indicator, the Department will make a second survey without additional charge. Upon failure of the Department's indicator to locate the tap after two attempts, the Department will assume responsibility to locate and plug the tap. No refund or credit will be allowed if indicator fails to locate the tap. The receipt for use of the indicator shall be on the job at the time appointed for the test.

Sizes of Taps and Service Pipes.

119. The size of tap and service pipe to supply a premises shall be based upon the water demand load of the premises as determined by "fixture units." In premises used for commercial and industrial purposes where it is not feasible to determine the size of the tap and service pipe on the basis of "fixture units" the sizes shall be based upon the water demand load of the premises. The minimum size of tap shall be ¾ inch and the minimum size service pipe shall be one (1) inch in diameter.

Copies of tables for determining the sizes of taps and service pipes are on file in each borough office of the Bureau of Water Supply.

The gooseneck as specified in Rule 140 shall be the same size as the service pipe.

Fire Connections.

120. The size of connections for fire services shall be subject to the approval of this Department. If the connection proposed exceeds 4 inches in diameter plans of the fire installation shall accompany the request filed for approval. The size of the fire service pipes installed under the Multiple Dwelling Law will be determined by the Department of Buildings.

The size of the corporation stop or wet connection for fire service pipes up to and including 4 inches in diameter shall be the same size as the fire service pipe. The size of the wet connection for fire service pipes larger than 4 inches in diameter shall be one size smaller than the size of the fire service pipe. (See Section C26-1346.0 Paragraph B-1959 of the Administrative Building Code).

Dual Fire and Commercial Service.

121A. A connection for commercial purposes may be made from a metered fire sprinkler line of 4 inches or larger in diameter, provided a meter is installed on the commercial branch line. Such connection shall be taken from the inlet side of the fire meter control valve and the method of connection shall be subject to the approval of the Department. On a 4-inch fire line, the connection shall not exceed 1½ inches in diameter. On a fire line 6 inches or larger in diameter, the size of the connection shall not exceed 2 inches.

Dual Fire and Domestic Service.

121B. A connection for domestic purposes may be made from a sprinkler line as permitted under Subdivision 16 of Section 4 and Section 248 of the Multiple Dwelling Law, in the manner as follows:

A house service water supply connection may be taken from the sprinkler water supply connection to the public main, on the house side of the main shut-off valve for the building, provided the diameter of the house service water supply connection does not exceed one-half the diameter of the sprinkler water supply connection. Only one connection of the domestic water supply to the sprinkler water supply shall be permitted, and no shut-off valve shall be placed on the sprinkler supply line other than the main shut-off valve for the building on the street side of the house service water supply connection. If such a connection is made and if a tap exists for the domestic purpose, the tap shall be plugged.

121C. Fire lines shall not be cross-connected with any system of piping within buildings except as permitted in Rule 121A and B.

Plumbers'   122. Advance notice shall be given by the plumber to the bor-
Appointments.   ough office of the Bureau of Water Supply, fixing the date on
                       which he wishes a tap or plug inserted. The plumber shall also
make an appointment with the Bureau of Water Supply to afford inspection before backfilling is placed on new or repaired service pipes. Advance notice of 24 hours, or of such
time as the Department may determine, will be required for this appointment. The
Department does not guarantee the insertion of a corporation stop, three-way connection
or placing of a wet connection on the day for which the appointment has been made with
the plumber, but will perform the work as soon as it is practicable.

Delay in Tap   123. If the plumber is not ready for the insertion of a tap or
of Service   plug, or the inspection of a service pipe installation, or repair on
Inspection.   the date and time for which an appointment had been made, but
                       not cancelled at least twenty-four (24) hours in advance of the
time for the appointment, the plumber shall be personally liable for the costs and expenses
incurred by the Department by reason of his non-readiness.

If a new appointment is required, it shall be made through the borough office of the
Bureau of Water Supply.

Size of   124. Sizes of excavations for wet connections and corporation
Excavation.   stops shall be in accordance with the following table:

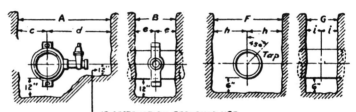

IF OBSTRUCTION PREVENTS USE
OF RACKET ABOVE SHAFT, THEN MAKE NOT
LESS THAN 3'-0" SO THAT RACHET CAN
BE WORKED UNDERNEATH THE SHAFT.

WET CONNECTIONS							CORPORATION STOPS				
SIZE		DIMENSIONS OF OPENINGS					SIZE	DIMENSIONS OF OPENINGS			
CONNECTION	WATER PIPE	A	B	c	d	e	WATER PIPE	F	G	h	i
2"	6"	6'-10"	4'-0"	1'-0"	5'-10"	2'-0"	4"	4'-4"	3'-0"	2'-2"	1'-6"
"	8"	7'-0"	"	1'-1"	5'-11"	"	6"	4'-6"	"	2'-3"	"
3" AND 4"	6"	6'-2"	"	1'-0"	7'-2"	"	8"	4'-8"	"	2'-4"	"
" " "	8"	8'-4"	"	1'-1"	7'-3"	"	12"	5'-0"	"	2'-6"	"
" " "	12"	8'-8"	"	1'-3"	7'-5"	"	16"	5'-4"	"	2'-8"	"
" " "	16"	9'-1"	"	1'-5"	7'-8"	"	20"	5'-8"	"	2'-10"	"
" " "	20"	9'-5"	"	1'-7"	7'-10	"	24"	6'-0"	"	3'-0"	"
6"	8"	8'-7"	5'-0"	1'-1"	7'-6"	2'-6"	30"	6'-4"	"	3'-8"	"
"	12"	9'-0"	"	1'-3"	7'-9"	"	36"	7'-0"	"	3'-6"	"
"	16"	9'-4"	"	1'-5"	7'-11"	"	48"	8'-0"	"	4'-0"	"
"	20"	9'-8"	"	1'-7"	8'-1"	"					
"	24"	10'-0"	"	2'-6"	8'-3"	"					
"	30"	10'-7"	"	2'-9"	8'-7"	"					
"	36"	11'-1"	"	3'-0"	8'-10"	"					
"	48"	12'-1"	"	3'-6"	9'-4"	"					
8"	12"	9'-2"	"	1'-3"	7'-11"	"					
"	16"	9'-6"	"	1'-5"	8'-1"	"					
"	20"	9'-10"	"	1'-7"	8'-3"	"					
"	24"	10'-2"	"	2'-6"	8'-5"	"					
"	30"	10'-8"	"	2'-9"	8'-6"	"					
"	36"	11'-3"	"	3'-0"	9'-0"	"					
"	48"	12'-3"	"	3'-6"	9'-6"	"					

WHERE TWO CORPORATON STOPS
ARE PLACED N THE SAME OPEN-
ING MAKE G 4'-0" CORPORATION
STOPS UP TO AND INCLUDING
1" IN SIZE, AND 5'-0" FOR COR-
PORATION STOPS 2" IN SIZE.

If subsurface conditions make it impracticable for a plumber to make an excavation
of the dimensions indicated herein, the plumber shall so notify the borough office of the
Bureau of Water Supply. That office shall then determine if the dimensions may be
changed and, if so, what the new dimensions shall be.

All excavations shall be made safe by sheathing and bracing, where necessary. The plumber shall be responsible for the safety of the excavation and backfill and shall be subject to the conditions stated in Section 5 of the Rules and Regulations fixing uniform annual charges.

Maintenance of Driven Tap.   125. Where a driven corporation stop is uncovered by a public service corporation, subway contractor or other individual, the public service corporation, contractor or other individual will be required to maintain and protect the stop during the construction work and pay the cost of its replacement with a screw corporation stop if it is disturbed in any manner. Just prior to backfilling the excavation the Department will replace, without cost the driven corporation stop with a screw stop and connect it to the existing service when, in its judgment, such replacement is necessary.

Demolition and Retention of Tap and Service.   126. Where plans have been filed with the Department of Buildings for a new structure and the water can be supplied through an existing tap, the tap may remain, upon the owner's application, provided that both the tap and service pipe conform with the current regulations as to size and materials.

(See Section 734 (1)-7.0 of the Administrative Code).

Leak at Tap or Service Pipe.   127. When tests made by the Department indicate that there is a leak at a tap or on a service pipe, and where conditions permit, a three-day notice to repair will be served upon the owner or occupant. If the notice is not complied with the Department will shut the tap and charge the expenses incurred to the owner.

Notice to Repair Tap or Service.   128. When the tap of a leaking service pipe is shut off by the Department the owner or his agent will be notified immediately, engage a licensed plumber to take over the street excavation and make the necessary repairs. If the owner fails to engage a licensed plumber the tap will be left closed and the excavation backfilled immediately. A notice to repair the service will then be served upon the owner or occupant.

Abandonment of Service Pipe.   129. If a tap has been shut off by 'the Department or owner's plumber and the service connected thereto is not to be used, the owner's plumber shall, after having secured the necessary permit, plug the tap and remove a portion of the abandoned service pipe at the point of entry into the building. Any meter covering the abandoned service pipe shall be physically removed, under permit, and any curb box over the abandoned service pipe shall also be removed.

Shut-Off of Tap by Licensed Plumber.   130. A licensed plumber may open or shut off a tap controlling a service pipe for repair, replacement or installation for which a permit has been issued. In the event that in making a repair, replacement or installation of a service pipe it is necessary to shut off a water main, such shut off shall be made only by the Department. The cost of shutting off the main will be charged to the plumber.

SERVICES

Service Pipe.   131. A service pipe is defined as that portion of the water pipe extending from the public water main to the house control valve, the building or to a point where the supply is fully metered.

Materials for Service Pipes.   132. Only new materials shall be used for installation or repair of service pipes. New service pipes of two inches in diameter or less may be of lead, brass (with the exception mentioned below) or copper, at option of owner. Service pipes larger than two inches in diameter may be of brass, (with the exception mentioned below) extra heavy galvanized iron or galvanized steel, or cast iron, at option of owner. The use of brass pipe, however, will not be approved if the water supply is furnished entirely from wells.

Except for the gooseneck, as specified in Rule No. 140, the material and diameter of a new service pipe shall be the same from the tap up to and into the building or to' a point where service is fully metered. On lead services, however, where it is not practicable to set the meter close to the building or vault wall, extra heavy galvanized iron or brass pipe may be used, instead of lead pipe, between the inner face of the wall and the meter, provided that the lead service pipe is carried through the wall and a valve placed at this point, and provided further that the pipe extension between the valve and the meter is exposed to view.

For lead service supplying sprinkler or standpipe systems, the section of the service extending inward from the outside face of the building wall shall be of approved material other than lead.

FITTINGS AND PIPE OF MATERIAL OTHER THAN SPECIFIED IN THESE REGULATIONS MUST BE INDIVIDUALLY APPROVED BY THE DEPARTMENT.

Pipe approved for use under these rules shall conform to the following types and their applicable specifications as hereinafter given:

Type of Pipe	Applicable Specifications
Lead	Department of Purchase 32-P-14: 50 T
Brass and Copper	Department of Purchase 32-P-3: 51 T
Copper Tubing	Department of Purchase 32-T-1: 50 T
Welded and Seamless Galvanized Steel	A.S.T.M. Designation A-120
Extra Heavy Galvanized Steel	A.S.T.M. Designation A-120
Galvanized Welded Wrought Iron	A.S.T.M. Designation A-120
Cast Iron	A.S.A. Standard Class 25

Dimensions and Weights. 133. Dimensions and weights of pipe approved for use under these rules are as follows:

Specification 32-P-14: 50 T, Dept. of Purchase

AA LEAD PIPE

Size (Nominal Inside Diameter) Inches	Wall Thickness in Inches	Weight per Linear Foot
¾	0.231	3½ lbs.
1	0.246	4¾ lbs.
1¼	0.258	6 lbs.
1½	0.288	8 lbs.
2	0.376	13¾ lbs.

AAA LEAD PIPE

Size (Nominal Inside Diameter) Inches	Wall Thickness in Inches	Weight per Linear Foot
¾	0.293	4¾ lbs.
1	0.298	6 lbs.
1¼	0.320	7¾ lbs.
1½	0.386	11¼ lbs.
2	0.504	19½ lbs.

Specification 32-P-3:51 T, Department of Purchase
RED BRASS AND COPPER PIPE

Nominal Dimensions Size of Pipe Inches	Actual Outside Diameter Inches	Wall Thickness Inches	Copper Pounds per Linear Foot	Red Brass 85% Pounds per Linear Foot
¾	1.050	0.114	1.30	1.27
1	1.315	0.126	1.82	1.78
1¼	1.660	0.146	2.69	2.63
1½	1.900	0.150	3.20	3.13
2	2.375	0.156	4.22	4.12
2½	2.875	0.187	6.12	5.99
3	3.500	0.219	8.75	8.56
3½	4.000	0.250	11.4	11.2
4	4.500	0.250	12.9	12.7
5	5.562	0.250	16.2	15.8
6	6.625	0.250	19.4	19.0
8	8.625	0.312	31.6	30.9
10	10.750	0.365	46.2	45.2

Specification A.S.T.M. A-120
STANDARD WEIGHTS AND DIMENSIONS OF WELDED AND SEAMLESS GALVANIZED STEEL PIPE
"Standard" Pipe

Size (Nominal Inside Diameter) Inches	Outside Diameter Inches	Number of Threads per Inch	Wall Thickness Inches	Weight of Pipe per Lin. Ft. Threaded and with Couplings, Lb.
¾	1.050	14	0.113	1.13
1	1.315	11½	0.133	1.68
1¼	1.660	11½	0.140	2.28
1½	1.900	11½	0.145	2.73
2	2.375	11½	0.154	3.68
2½	2.875	8	0.203	5.82
3	3.500	8	0.216	7.62
3½	4.000	8	0.226	9.20
4	4.500	8	0.237	10.89
5	5.563	8	0.258	14.81
6	6.625	8	0.280	19.18
8	8.625	8	0.322	29.35
10	10.750	8	0.365	41.85

Specification A.S.T.M. A-120
STANDARD WEIGHTS AND DIMENSIONS OF GALVANIZED WELDED WROUGHT IRON PIPE
"Standard" Weight Pipe

Size (Nominal Inside Diameter) Inches	Outside Diameter Inches	Number of Threads per Inch	Wall Thickness Inches	Weight of Pipe per Lin. Ft. Threaded and with Couplings, Lb.
¾	1.050	14	0.115	1.13
1	1.315	11½	0.136	1.68
1¼	1.660	11½	0.143	2.28
1½	1.900	11½	0.148	2.73
2	2.375	11½	0.158	3.68
2½	2.875	8	0.208	5.82
3	3.500	8	0.221	7.62
3½	4.000	8	0.231	9.20
4	4.500	8	0.242	10.89
5	5.563	8	0.263	14.81
6	6.625	8	0.286	19.19
8	8.625	8	0.329	28.81
10	10.750	8	0.372	41.13

Specification 32-T-1:50 T, Department of Purchase
COPPER TUBING

Nominal Size Inches	Actual Outside Diameter Inches	Wall Thickness Inches	Type K Nominal Weight Per foot Pounds
¾	0.875	.065	0.641
1	1.125	.065	0.839
1¼	1.375	.065	1.04
1½	1.625	.072	1.36
2	2.125	.083	2.06
2½	2.315	2.875	7.67
3	2.892	3.5	10.25
3½	3.364	4.00	12.51
4	3.818	4.5	14.97
6	5.741	6.625	28.58

Specification A.S.T.M. A-120
EXTRA HEAVY GALVANIZED STEEL PIPE

Nominal Size Inches	Diameter Inside Inches	Outside Inches	Lbs. Per Linear Feet
1	.951	1.315	2.17
1¼	1.272	1.660	3.0
1½	1.494	1.900	3.63
2	1.933	2.375	5.02
2½	2.315	2.875	7.66
3	2.892	3.5	10.25
3½	3.364	4.00	12.51
4	3.818	4.5	14.98
6	5.751	6.625	28.57
8	7.625	8.625	43.39
10	9.75	10.750	54.74
12	11.75	12.750	65.42

Specification A.S.A. Standard Class 25
CAST IRON PIPE (CLASS "B" CORPORATION)

Size	Diameter Outside Inches	Wall Thickness Inches	Barrel Weight Pounds Per Foot
3	3.96	0.38	13.3
4	5.00	0.44	19.7
6	6.90	0.48	30.2
8	9.05	0.52	43.5
10	11.10	0.56	59.5
12	13.20	0.60	74.1

Cast iron pipe shall be cement lined in accordance with this Department's specifications and coated on the outside with a coal tar pitch.

High Pressure Services

134. Where lead pipe is used for a service in which the pressure is 70 pounds per square inch or more, such lead shall be in conformity with specifications for AAA lead pipe.

Wiped and Flared Joints.

135. All connections between lead and iron pipes shall be made with extra heavy brass soldering nipples and "wiped" solder joints. Connections between lead pipes and lead, brass and copper pipes, (excluding copper tubing) shall be made by means of wiped solder joints not less than 2½ inches in length, properly prepared, tinned and fused. All joints shall be uniform and of the size known to the plumbing trade as "Heavy." All wiped joints shall be made by use of pot, ladle and cloth. Use of a torch to accomplish the wiping of a solder joint will not be permitted except by authorization of the department when conditions make the use of pot, ladle and cloth impracticable. The solder used shall be composed of 60% lead and 40% tin and the outside diameter of the wiped joint at the center shall be at least ¾ inch in excess of the outside diameter of the lead, brass or copper pipe.

Soldering nipples shall be of extra heavy cast brass or thoroughly annealed seamless drawn extra heavy brass pipe of standard iron pipe gauge. Joints on copper tubing service pipes may be of the flared type.

Caulked Joints.

136. The caulked joints for cast iron service pipes shall be made as follows:

The spigot end of the pipe shall be inserted into the hub to approximately the full depth, and the space between the spigot and the hub shall be equalized. The inner portion of the annular space between the spigot and hub shall first be packed with solid, molded or tubular rubber rings, asbestos rope, or with other clean, sound packing material of an approved type which does not breed bacteria. The remaining space in the hub shall then be run full of lead at one pouring and the joint shall be well caulked with proper tools and made watertight. In pouring the joint sufficient metal shall be provided, so that when the joint is caulked the lead shall be flush with the face of the hub. The lead used shall be of the best quality, pure soft lead, practically free from all impurities; it shall show upon analysis not less than 99.5% by weight of pure metallic lead. No cold lead shall be used for caulking or filling in. The depth of lead joints for 4-inch, 6-inch, and 8-inch pipe shall be two and three-eight inches and for 12-inch, 16-inch, 20-inch and 24-inch pipe, three inches. (See sketch on following page).

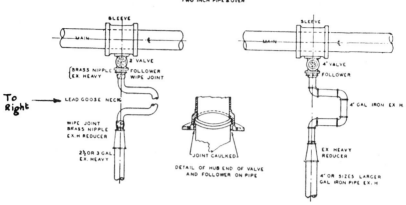

METHOD FOR CONNECTING SERVICE PIPE
WITH SMITH CONNECTION
TWO INCH PIPE & OVER

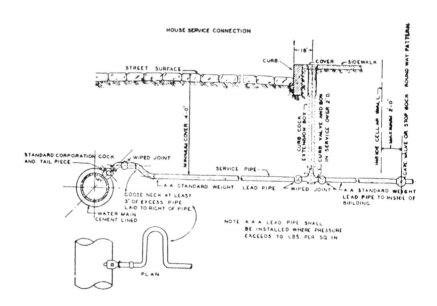

HOUSE SERVICE CONNECTION

House Control Valves.	137. The house control valve shall be of the gate type. It shall be placed in the service pipe inside the building within 2 feet of the front building wall and be so located as to be accessible at all times.

All valves shall be designed for a 150 lbs. minimum working pressure, as specified in the manufacturer's catalogue, and may be of the outside stem and yoke type.

Curb Valves.	138. Curb valves shall be installed on all fire service pipes. Curb valves shall be installed on all other service pipes over 2 inches in diameter. On service pipes 2 inches or less in diameter the curb

valves and boxes may be set at the option of the owner. The curb valves shall be set in the service pipe in the sidewalk area at or within 2 feet of the curb. If the water main is within the sidewalk area the curb valve shall be placed between the main and the building line. Curb valves shall be of the gate type, non-rising stem valve, designed for a minimum of 150 pounds per square inch working pressure.

Access to all curb valves installed shall be provided by a tar coated iron extension box with cover, the cover to be flush with the sidewalk level. Curb valves 2 inches and less in diameter may be equipped with a wheel for operation, provided a permanent ½-inch iron rod is attached thereto and extended to the top of the curb box. No curb valve shall be installed in a driveway.

Curb valves larger than 2 inches in diameter shall be equipped with an operating nut at least 1¼" square and no extension rod need be attached thereto. Such operating nut may be installed on curb valves 2 inches and less in diameter at the option of the owner.

In sprinkler and fire line installations, the location of the sidewalk control valve will be governed by Sections C26-1346.0, Par. B & C and C26-1407.0 of Paragraph A of the Administrative Code.

Services To Be Straight. 139. Each new service pipe shall be laid in a straight line at right angles to the street main and extending from the tap to the main house control valve. Where the surface or subsurface conditions made it impracticable to install a service pipe in accordance with the above conditions, it may be otherwise laid, provided the plumber submits a plan showing the proposed alternative location of the service pipe, and procures the written approval of the department. The driving of a service pipe through the ground is prohibited.

Gooseneck on Service Pipe. 140. Unless otherwise authorized by the Bureau of Water Supply, each lead and copper tubing service pipe shall have an excess of at least three feet of pipe formed in a gooseneck at the connection to the tap and laid to the right hand, facing the tap. Unless otherwise authorized by the Bureau of Water Supply, each brass, copper and galvanized steel service shall have, at the last wet connection, or an offset swing joint consisting of four elbows and three pieces of pipe each not less than 2 feet in length, laid to the right side facing the connection. Connections to the City main by cast iron pipe may be made direct; no offset swing joint will be required.

Where buildings are constructed on pile foundations or other unyielding supports, the service pipes shall have two goosenecks, or two offset swing joints, one at the tap and one immediately outside the building (laid to the right facing the building) with a sleeve to carry the service through the foundation wall.

140A. Clearance shall be provided around service pipe passing through wall to protect against:

(a) Chemical action from direct contact with concrete.

(b) Distortion or rupture of service pipe from shearing action due to settlement.

(c) Distortion or rupture of service pipe caused by expansion or contraction.

Sleeves or arches may be used to provide the wall opening. Clearance shall not be less than ½" between the outside of the pipe and the wall. The space between the pipe and the wall structure shall be carefully packed or caulked with lead, or water-proof material-resistant to vermin and rodents.

Cover for Service Pipe. 141. All service pipes shall be installed and maintained at a depth of at least four (4) feet and no more than six (6) feet below the ground unless written permission to vary this requirement is obtained from the Department. Where a service pipe has less than four (4) feet of cover, due to subsurface conditions, it shall be insulated and protected, if required, in a manner approved by the Department.

A service pipe shall not be laid within twelve (12") inches of any other sub-surface structure, conduit or pipe, nor directly below and parallel with such sub-surface structure, conduit or pipe.

**Service in
Sewer
Trench.**

142. Service pipe laid in a sewer or construction trench shall be protected from settlement by supports or by securely benching the service in side earth wall.

**Service
in Subway
Air Vent.**

143. Where service pipe is installed through a subway air vent or similar construction, the method of installation shall be made as illustrated below:

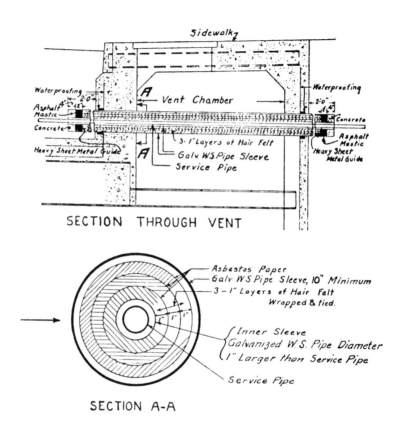

SECTION THROUGH VENT

SECTION A-A

Backfill.

144. After a tap has been inserted or service pipe installed, the backfill around and one foot over the main and service shall be of clean earth, free from stone and carefully tamped under and around the main and service. The remainder of the backfill shall be free from stones larger than 3 inches in diameter and shall be satisfactorily compacted either by tamping or flushing, or both.

Where tunneling has been permitted the backfilling of the tunnel portion shall be well compacted with clean fill free of stones.

**Test of
Service
Pipe.**

145. Each new service pipe or repaired service pipe shall be subjected to a water test under the street main pressure by the plumber in the presence of the tapper or inspector. All pipes and appurtenances shall remain uncovered for the duration of the test and shall show no sign of leakage. Subject to the discretion of the Department when any question arises as to the installation being in conformity with these regulations, internal hydrostatic test as specified for materials may be applied. For delay in Inspection of Services, see Rule No. 123.

Service Repairs. 146. If the repair requires the necessity for the replacement of more than one-half of the service pipe, and the old service or remainder thereof is not in conformity with these regulations, an entire new service pipe shall be installed to conform with the rules relating to new service pipe; if less than one-half requires replacement, the new section installed shall conform to the rules governing new services.

Repairs to Gooseneck. 147. When a repair to a service pipe involves the uncovering of the tap, and the gooseneck or offset swing is found to be insufficient or is lacking, a proper gooseneck or offset swing joint shall be installed.

Service Pipe Damaged by Electrolysis, Galvanic Action, Etc. 148. When a service pipe is damaged by electrolysis, galvanic action or other local condition, it shall be repaired, in a manner satisfactory to this Department, and protected against such damage in the future. This expense shall be charged to the owner.

Electrical Thawing. 149. Thawing of water services or mains by the use of electric current shall be performed only under special permit of this Department and through the agency of a licensed electrician, an electric utility corporation, or other individual or corporation having qualifications and equipment approved by this Department. The operation of thawing services shall be supervised by an Inspector assigned by the Department.

Private Mains. 150. Permits for the installation or the maintenance of a private main to any property, whether such private main is laid in a public or private street, will be issued subject to the following restrictions and terms:

a. The owner or owners installing a private main shall file an agreement to the effect that any property facing the street, road or right-of-way in which the main is installed will be entitled to connect to the private main upon the owner of such property sharing with the owner or owners of the private main the cost of the installation of the private main, provided that the private main is of sufficient size to supply the additional premises.

b. Owners of the private main shall be responsible for the maintenance and repair of the private main and for any expense incurred to the City by reason of defects developing in the private main.

c. Private mains and all connections thereto and branches therefrom, shall be installed or repaired only under permit and inspection of this Department. Permits for connections, extensions or repairs subsequent to the original installation will be granted only upon the written consent of the owner or owners of the private main.

d. Private mains shall be at least 1 inch in diameter and may be of cast iron, standard galvanized iron, lead, red brass or copper pipe.

e. A private main shall be controlled by a gate valve placed on the building line of the street where it connects with the City main and a cast iron extension street box placed over the valve. An additional valve and box shall be installed to control each 1,000 linear feet section of the private main and at each branch connection where a lateral private main is extended.

f. Taps and service connections to private mains shall comply with regulations governing tap and service pipe installations, in force at the time of the installation.

Plugging Private Main Service Connections. 151. If a service connection to a private main is to be abandoned, it shall be disconnected at the tap or stop valve at the connection to the private main and a plug inserted. This work shall be performed at the owner's expense by a licensed plumber under permit from this Department.

Elimination of Private Mains, Driven Corporation Stops and Transferring of Taps and Services. 152. The procedure to be followed in replacement of City mains and elimination of temporary or private water mains, driven corporation stops and transferring services therefrom to City mains is:

a. Where it becomes necessary to lay, relay, lower or raise a water main due to the grading of the street, where such street was not previously at the established grade, necessitating the altering or extending of house services, the Department will furnish and install a new tap for each property owner whose premises were connected directly with the main as previously laid. Reconnection of the service to the new tap and any extension of the service or the relaying of same as required by these rules shall be done by and at the expense of the owner, in accordance with Sec. 734(4)-6.1 of the Administrative Code of the City of New York.

b. Where it becomes necessary to lay or relay a city main due to change in the established line or grade of a street, or for distribution purposes, the transferring of taps and connections to service to the exent necessary to restore the water supply will be done by and at the expense of the Department. Where the service pipe has less than four feet or more than six feet of cover, the owner at his own expense shall relay the service pipe with the minimum cover.

c. When a city water main is installed, all owners of houses fronting on the City main and receiving a supply from a private main shall disconnect their house services from the private main and connect with the City main. This work shall be done within 10 days or in such other period as may be specified by the Department. A tap of the appropriate size will be provided and installed by the Department without cost to the owner, provided the owner had previously paid the City for a tap or for permit for the tapping of the private main in an amount equivalent to the cost of the tap. The expense of altering or connecting the house service pipe to the tap shall be borne by the owner. The tap to which the private main is attached to the City main will be removed and dismantled by the Department without charge. Penalty for failure to transfer house services under this regulation is provided in Section 734 (4)-6.1 of the Administrative Code.

Meters;
When to be
Placed.

153. a. An approved water meter shall be installed in all places occupied for business purposes which is supplied by city water. (Administrative Code, Section 734 (4)-1.0.)

b. A building used for business occupancy shall not have more than one meter set at point of entry on each service supplying the building.

c. In a building used for both business and dwelling purposes, the water supply to the business portion shall be metered by the use of only one meter. This may be accomplished by either having a separate metered service to the business portion or arranging the piping in the building so that one meter shall measure the supply to said business portion. If the hot water supply to the business portion of a building, used for both business and dwelling purposes is from a central hot water system, the hot water supply to said business portion shall be metered by the use of only one hot water meter.

d. Unmetered city water shall not be used in any premises where the supply is recorded as fully metered, or in that part of any premises that is recorded as being supplied through a meter or meters.

e. The Commissioner is authorized to install or cause to be installed a meter or meters in any premises where repeated violation notices to prevent waste of water are necessary, or where the owner fails to comply with waste of water violation notices. (See Administrative Code, Section 734 (4)-4.1.)

f. All water used in the construction of buildings of seven or more stories in height shall be metered. Prior to the commencement of actual building operations, a meter of proper size shall be installed on each tap or service supplying the premises. It shall be placed in an accessible location at a point to be designated by the Department. It shall be close to the point of entry of the service pipe, and shall be enclosed in a vault or box of ample size and substantial construction which will provide adequate protection against damage or injury from frost or any other cause. Each meter shall remain in service throughout the entire period of building operation, and subsequently until such time as the annual water charges for the structure become effective or the permanent meter has been installed. In the event that the meter has not covered the water service to the premises or has not been maintained in good working order during the entire period of building operations, the charge for water consumed during such building operations shall be established as provided by the rules and regulations fixing charges.

g. 1. Fire lines in buildings used for business purposes shall be metered. Fire lines in metered domestically occupied buildings, unmetered buildings or partially metered buildings may be installed on an annual rate basis, except that in partially metered premises, if the fire line is confined to the metered business section, the fire line shall also be metered.

2. The use of water through meters approved for fire sprinkler systems only is prohibited for any other use except the testing of the fire sprinkler system.

Meter Permits.
154a. Permits are required to set, reset, repair or disconnect a water meter. Application for permits shall be made to the Bureau of Water Register by a licensed plumber duly authorized by the owner.

b. Meter repair permits may be issued to authorized meter repair companies for the repair, on the premises, of cold water meter three inches in size and larger.

c. No hot water meters shall be repaired on the premises.

d. Within twenty-four hours or not later than the next working day following the completion of any work for which a meter permit has been issued, the permit, carrying a certification of the date of completion of the work, shall be returned to the borough office of the Bureau of Water Register.

155. THE FOLLOWING WATER METERS ARE APPROVED FOR USE IN THE CITY OF NEW YORK:

DISC METERS

Arctic (frostproof)	¾″ to 1″
American (frostproof)	¾″ to 1″
*American (disc)	1½″ to 6″
Badger (frostproof) disc	¾″ to 1″
*Badger-Disc Model SC	1½″ to 4″
Empire #12 (frostproof)	¾″ to 1″
Hersey-Disc HF (frostproof)	¾″ to 1″
*Hersey-Disc HD	1½″ to 3″
Keystone Disc	3 ″
Rockwell-Type 6 Disc	1½″ to 2″
Trident (frostproof)	¾″ to 1″
Trident (split case) Hot Water	⅝″ to 2″
*Trident-Style 3	1½″ to 4″
Worthington Gamon Watchdog (frostproof)	¾″ to 1″
*Worthington Gamon Watchdog Disc	1½″ to 6″

* INCLUDES HOT WATER METERS ⅝″ to 2.″

CURRENT TYPE METERS **

Badger Turbine	2″ to 12″
Eureka-Model B	2″ to 6″
Gem-Model AAX	8″ to 12″
Hersey Torrent	2″ to 12″
Trident Crest	2″ to 12″
Trident Full Flow Crest	3″ to 6″
Worthington Gamon Watchdog	2″ to 8″
Worthington Turbine-1-H	2″ to 8″

COMPOUND METERS **

Badger	2″ to 10″
Hersey (bronze case)	2″ to 6″
Hersey (iron case) CT-2-10	8″ to 10″
Rockwell	2″ to 6″
Trident	3″ to 10″
Trident (Neptune) Full Flow	3″ to 6″
Worthington Gamon Watchdog	2″ to 6″

** SEE RULE NO. 156.

FIRE LINE METERS

Hersey Detector H. F.	3″ to 12″
Trident Protectus	4″ to 10″

Approved for Sewer Rent Use Only

Badger—Measure Rite	2″ to 12″
Sparling	2″ to 12″

156. Current and compound types of water meters may be installed only upon approval of the Bureau of Water Register upon filing of satisfactory proof that the quantity of water required will be drawn at a rate to insure proper registration.

157. a. No used or repaired meter shall be installed to cover a service at a new location unless specific request for the setting of such meter is made in writing by the owner of the property.

b. All used meters shall be repaired and conform to the Department regulation on accuracy and approved under permit before being set at a new location.

Sizing of Meters.

158. a. A meter shall be restricted to a size and type that will insure accurate registration on the basis of the water requirements of the premises or portion of the premises to be metered.

b. A meter shall not be larger than the service or pipe supplying the meter.

c. Where a meter is supplied through a connection made to fire line or sprinkler service pipe, for commercial or domestic purposes, it shall not exceed the size of the permitted connection and shall conform to the regulations on setting meters.

d. Where inaccuracy of registration is found to be due to the improper size and/or type of meter, such meter shall be replaced by a meter of a size and type to be designated by the Department. When such change of meter size is effected, the piping of the meter setting from the discharge side of the inlet valve to the discharge side of the outlet valve shall be of the same size as the meter.

e. The minimum size cold water meter for new installations and replacement shall be ¾″. Existing ⅝″ cold water meters may be repaired and reset at their present locations, excepting when they supply air conditioning or refrigeration, or when consumption indicates that the meter is undersized. The minimum size hot water meter may be ⅝″.

Meter Test.

159. Before being installed, every new, used or repaired meter shall be sent to a designated Department station for testing. The Commissioner of the Department of Water Supply, Gas and Electricity shall establish charges for the testing of water meters performed by the Department. Such charge shall be paid to the Bureau of Water Register at the time of making the application.

Setting of Meters.

160. Meters shall be set or reset as shown in the following drawings of typical settings and meet the following requirements.

a. The meter shall be set horizontal, the dial facing upward and not more than three feet above the floor, and properly supported.

b. 1. Disc meters shall be set within one foot of the inlet meter control valve.

b. 2. In the setting of Current and Compound meters, a straight section of pipe, eight times the diameter of the size of the meter shall be installed between the inlet meter control valve and the meter connection. No fitting shall be permitted in the straight sction of pipe. If a shorter length of pipe is permitted the meter shall be calibrated in place at owner's expense. Where fish traps are permitted by the department they shall be installed immediately after the inlet meter control valve.

TYPICAL METER SETTING

$\frac{3}{4}$" & 1" METER SETTING

ALL VALVES GATE TYPE

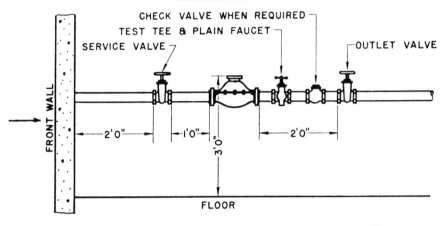

CHECK VALVE WHEN REQUIRED
TEST TEE & PLAIN FAUCET
SERVICE VALVE
OUTLET VALVE
FRONT WALL
2'0"
1'0"
3'0"
2'0"
FLOOR

TYPICAL METER SETTING

$1\frac{1}{2}$" & LARGER METER SETTING

FOR CURRENT AND COMPOUND METERS LENGTH SHOULD
NOT BE LESS THAN EIGHT DIAMETERS OF PIPE. IF SHORTER
LENGTH IS USED, METER MUST BE CALIBRATED IN PLACE.

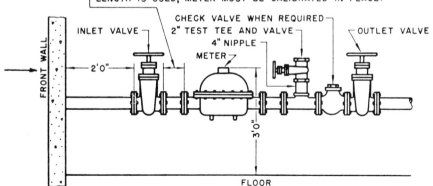

CHECK VALVE WHEN REQUIRED
INLET VALVE
2" TEST TEE AND VALVE
OUTLET VALVE
4" NIPPLE
METER
FRONT WALL
2'0"
3'0"
FLOOR

NO FITTING PERMITTED BETWEEN INLET VALVE AND METER.
NO CONNECTION TO TEST TEE PERMITTED.
ON $1\frac{1}{2}$" AND 2" METERS TEST TEE AND VALVE SHALL BE
SAME SIZE AS METER.
ON 3" AND LARGER METERS TEST TEE & VALVE SHALL BE 2"

TYPICAL METER SETTING

COMMERCIAL AND FIRE SPRINKLER METER SETTING
(WHEN PERMITTED)

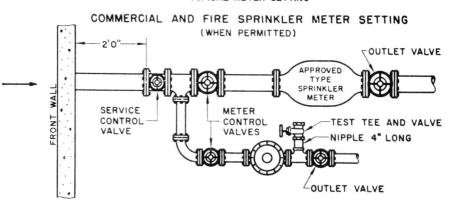

c. Connections shall be made by coupling, union or flange union or approved compression fittings on both inlet and outlet ends of meter and bored for sealing with holes not less than one-eight (⅛") of an inch in diameter.

d. Unions or couplings are prohibited in the outlet piping of a meter that would permit removal of the meter setting without the breaking of the seal wiring.

e. When a meter equipped with a check valve or check valves, to prevent backflow of water, is set on a service, a separate check valve is not required. Where such meter is removed, a check valve shall be installed in the service pipe until the meter is reset.

f. Any connection to a test tee is strictly prohibited.

g. All meter valves shall be standard gate valves.

h. Meters shall be set or reset so that they may be easily examined and read: In all premises where the supply of water is to be fully metered the meter shall be set within three feet of the building or vault wall at point of entry of service pipe. The service pipe between the meter control valve and the meter shall be kept exposed. When a building is situated back of the building line or conditions exist in a building that prevent the setting of the meter at a point of entry, the meter may be set outside of the building in a proper waterproof and frostproof pit, or at another location approved by the Bureau of Water Register.

i. Prior to the setting or resetting of a 3" or larger meter, Current or Compound, or meters to be set in pits when permitted, the plumber shall submit to the borough office of the Bureau of Water Register for approval, a plan or sketch in duplicate showing all details for the proposed installation.

j. IN ALL CASES THE METER SETTINGS SHALL BE TO THE SATISFACTION OF THE BUREAU OF WATER REGISTER.

Meter   161. By-passes around meters are prohibited, except those ap-
By-Pass.   proved by Bureau of Water Register, such as:
a. Tunnels where toxic fumes may endanger lives, etc.

b. In order to provide continuous service protection for piers and buildings having only one source of supply, which ordinarily would have to be shut down in order to test the accuracy of meter located therein.

If by-pass is permitted by the Bureau of Water Register, the installation shall conform to the following drawing:

TYPICAL METER SETTING
Including By-Pass

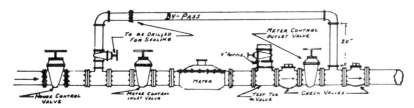

NOTE: By-pass to be of sufficient height so that top case and interior meter can be removed for repairs or replacement.

Meter Pit Requirements.   162. Meter pits shall be so constructed as to be waterproof and frostproof and be of sufficient size to permit easy access to all portions of the meter and connections with at least 1′ clearance on each side of meter. Pits less than 4′ in depth shall not be less than 2′6″ wide and 3′6″ long. Pits less than 4′ in depth shall be provided with a hinged cover not to exceed 40 lbs. in weight with suitable handle and so constructed as to permit the entire pit being uncovered. Pits 4′ or more in depth shall be provided with an access opening of at least 2′6″ square. The cover of such opening shall not exceed 40 lbs. in weight, shall be hinged and shall be provided with a suitable handle. Covers exceeding 40 lbs. weight shall be counter balanced. Pits 3′ or more in depth shall be provided with permanent steps or metal ladder.

Pits containing sewer traps shall be provided with an air vent.

See sketch below for typical meter pit construction.

TYPICAL METER VAULT

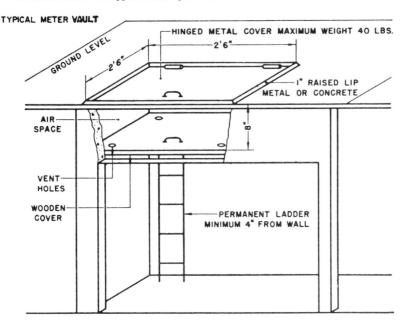

Meter Repairs.   163. a. The owner shall maintain the meter in good working order at all times and shall be responsible for its safeguarding and protection.

b. Meters removed from premises for repairs shall be delivered to the meter manufacturer or to a duly authorized meter repair company within three (3) working days from date of issue of permit. The number, size and style must correspond with the information stated in the Department permit.

c. Meter manufacturers and repair companies shall complete repairs to meters within two weeks of receipt of meters and forward them immediately to the Department Testing Station. Plumbers shall remove meters from the testing station and reset them within five (5) working days after Department notice of completion of test.

d. Cold water meters three inches in size and larger may be repaired on the premises. All meters repaired on premises are to be SET at ZERO, the repair company to furnish index before repairs, with certification that meter has been reset at zero after repairs were made. No hot water meters shall be repaired on the premises.

Removal of Meters.   164a. When approval is granted to transfer from a metered rate to an annual rate, the meter shall be removed under a permit from this Department.

b. If a meter shall have been discontinued without authority, it shall not be reset until a permit is obtained from this Department, the meter will be tested and set at zero, at the expense of the owner.

c. When a metered corporation stop or wet connection is destroyed, the meter shall be removed under permit from this Department.

Seals.   165. A seal placed by the Department for the protection of any meter, valve, fitting or other water connection shall not be tampered with or defaced. It shall not be broken except on written authorization of the Department. Where the seal is broken without authorization the Department reserves the right to order the meter removed for test and set at zero, at the expense of the owner. It is a violation of Section 1432 of the Penal Code to break or deface or cause to be broken the seal of a water meter. The owner shall be responsible for safeguarding and protecting the seal.

Meter Shut-Off.   166. In any premises where water is obtained through more than one meter, and where tests indicate that accurate registration is not being obtained by reason of the divided delivery of water through more than one meter, the Department reserves the right to shut off and seal one or more of the meters to insure accuracy of registration.

Plumber Selected When Owner Neglects.   167. The Department may select and order a plumber, on failure of the owner or occupant, to do the work indicated in the Department notice in respect to installation or repair of meters or correction of violations pertaining to metered connections, and all expense attached thereto will become a lien against the property, as provided for by Section 415-(1)-7.0 of the Administrative Code.

RULES AND REGULATIONS GOVERNING AND RESTRICTING USE AND SUPPLY OF WATER IN NEW YORK CITY
General Rules

Connection to Independent Water Supply Prohibited.   168. In any system of piping supplied by City Water, there shall be no connection to any other source of water supply. (See Administrative Code C26.1223.0 and 141.02 N. Y. C. Health Code.)

Direct Connections to Drainage System Prohibited.   169. Direct connection between water supply piping and any drainage system or vent piping is prohibited. (See Administrative Code Sec. C26-1223.0).

Chemical Water Treatment.   170. Chemical treatment of water used for human consumption is prohibited except by a licensed operator qualified by the Department of Health under the provisions of Section 141.07 of the Sanitary Code, and such treatment is to be limited to the chemicals and mixtures thereof as specified by that section. Chemical treatment apparatus approved by the Board of Standards and Appeals under provisions of Section 141.07 of the Sanitary Code must be submitted to the Department of Water Supply, Gas and Electricity for approval of methods of connections to water supply systems. Such apparatus shall also be subjected to siphonic tests to determine what check valves and vacuum breakers may be required in the installation to prevent contamination of the water supply by siphonage of chemicals, (in excess of the dilutions prescribed by Section 141.07 of the Sanitary Code), into the water supply system. Water supply connections to boilers, commercial equipment, or other apparatus requiring any form of chemical water treatment shall be adequately protected against backflow or siphonage of contaminated water into the water supply system, with check valves, vacuum breakers, or indirect connection, as required by the Department of Water Supply, Gas and Electricity. Plans for such installations must be approved by the Department.

Contamination   171. Where the Department of Water Supply, Gas and Electri-
of Water   city discovers that contamination does in fact exist, the water
Supply.   supply to the offending fixtures, apparatus, piping or appurtenances shall be shut off and the necessary remedial action taken.
In the event of failure to comply with these provisions, the penalties as set forth in Rule 176 shall become effective.

Priming   172. Pumps, other than those used for pumping City water,
Connections;   shall not be directly connected to the City water supply system.
Pumps.   Where City water is used for priming purposes, it shall be supplied
by means of an indirect water supply connection through an
open tank with the outlet of the direct water supply located at least two inches above the maximum overflow level of such tank.

Ship   173. Every connection to the City water supply on a pier,
Connections.   wharf or bulkhead, used or available as as ship or boat supply,
including hydrants, shall be equipped with a swing check valve
approved by the Department of Water Supply, Gas and Electricity, and shall be installed in a horizontal position immediately adjacent to the outlet of the control valve of the permanent water connection. The outlet of the check valve shall be equipped with a hose or union coupling to permit ready detachment for inspection and testing purposes.

Ball Stops   174. Water Supply inlets to roof tanks shall be located at least
and Roof   4 inches above the overflow pipe level of the tank and shall be
Tank.   equipped with an automatic ball stop. The outlet from a roof tank
to the distribution system in the building shall be effectively equipped to prevent solids from entering into such piping. All down feed supplies from a tank cross-connected in any manner with distribution supply piping in a building supplied by direct street main or pump pressure shall be equipped with check valve to prevent backflow of water into the roof tank. (See Administrative Code C26-1273.0)

The sizes and methods of connecting the overflow pipe from gravity and suction tanks shall be as provided in the Building Code.

Auxiliary   175. Where the City water is used as an auxiliary supply to a
Supply   roof or suction tank, which is also fed by a well, by salt water or
For Tank.   by other source of supply, the tank shall be an open one and the
pipe supplying City water thereto shall be controlled by a ballcock
and shall discharge at least four inches above the flood level rim of the tank.

(See Administrative Code Sec. 26.1273.0, 14.7.6.2b ballcock, 14.7.6.4d overflow.)

Penalty for   176. The penalty for violating any one of Rules 168, 169, 170,
Violation.   171-2-3-4-5 will be shutting off the water supply to the premises
and charging to the owner all expense incidental thereto. Service
will not be restored until violations have been properly removed and charges paid.

AIR CONDITIONING AND REFRIGERATION
RULE 177A
APPLICATIONS

Applications,   Application for permits to install refrigeration or air conditioning
Permits   equipment in any building supplied with water from the City-
and   owned water supply system shall be made by the owner of the
Definitions.   building or his agent prior to installation, and shall be properly
executed. All information requested shall be furnished thereon.
Approved copy of the application will be returned as a permit.

A permit from the Bureau of Water Register of the Department is required for the installation of all refrigeration and air conditioning equipment using City water. Such permit shall be subject to the requirements and provisions of Rule No. 100 of the Rules and Regulations Governing and Restricting Use and Supply of Water in New York City.

The following definitions shall be used:

A. "Refrigeration System" shall mean an installation for maintenance, by heat removal, of temperatures which are 60 deg. F. or less.

B. "Air Conditioning System" shall mean an installation for maintenance, by heat removal, of temperatures which are more than 60 deg. F.

C. "System" shall comprise an individual unit or the total of all individual units or aggregations of units or a combination of units within an entire building, whether or not all the units constituting such total aggregation or combination are under one ownership.

D. "City" shall mean the City of New York.

E. "Commissioner" shall mean the Commissioner of the Department of Water Supply, Gas & Electricity of the City of New York.

F. "Department" shall mean the Department of Water Supply, Gas and Electricity of the City of New York.

G. An "Installation" shall mean the total number of tons of refrigeration or air conditioning.

H. "Automatic Water Regulating Valve or Device" shall mean a self regulating valve or other device, the purpose of which shall limit the maximum use of City water, on units which do not have a water conserving device, to 1.5 G.P.M. per ton of refrigeration or air conditioning.

I. "Water conserving device" shall mean an evaporative condensor, water cooling tower, spray pond, economizer or similar apparatus, which device shall not consume City water for make-up purposes in excess of two (2) per cent of the amount that would normally be used without such device. In addition, there shall be allowed two (2) per cent of the amount of water that would normally be used without such device for purpose of bleeding and wash down.

Rating of Refrigeration and Air Conditioning Equipment shall be:

Rating of one ton of refrigeration and air conditioning is the removal of heat at the rate of 12,000 British Thermal Units per hour. The following equivalents will be used:

"Air Conditioning (Electric)." One horsepower of the compressor motor shall be equivalent to one ton of air conditioning.

"Refrigeration (Electric)." One horse power of the compressor motor shall be equivalent to 6/10 of a ton of refrigeration.

"Refrigeration and Air Conditioning (Gas)." Refrigeration or air conditioning equipment using gas fuel for energy shall be rated on the basis that one ton is equal to the removal of 12,000 British Thermal Units per hour.

"Refrigeration and Air Conditioning (Steam)." These installations all require a water conserving device. The manufacturer's tonnage shall be used.

RULE 177B

General Rules Pertaining to Air Conditioning and Refrigeration:

R-AC-1. Each direct water connection to a refrigeration or air conditioning unit using City water for cooling purposes shall be equipped with a check valve set not more than two (2) feet from the unit.

R-AC-2. Each unit containing more than 20 pounds of refrigerant shall be provided with a relief valve installed between the check valve and the unit, such relief valve being set at 5 pounds above the maximum water pressure at the point of installation.

R-AC-3. Where the refrigeration or air conditioning system is in excess of one-third (1/3) ton the City water supply to such system shall be metered.

R-AC-4. Where City water is piped to a water conserving device, the piping supplying such water shall discharge at least two (2) inches above the over-flow rim of the pan.

R-AC-5. The waste water from all systems having direct connection to the City water supply shall be discharged into a receptacle. The point of discharge (outlet of discharge piping) shall be located at least one (1) inch above the over-flow rim of said receptacle.

R-AC-6. Condensate, from steam used directly or indirectly to produce the cooling effect in air conditioning or refrigeration systems and then condensed by a stream of water flowing in the circuit of a water conserving device which uses City water for make-up purpose, shall be collected and used as part of the make-up water to the water conserving device on and after November 1, 1966 on all systems.

An exception to R-AC-6 shall be granted when the water from the steam is used as feed water to a boiler producing the steam.

RULE 177C

Pertaining to Refrigeration:

R-1. All refrigeration systems in excess of six (6) tons of rated capacity using City water, heretofore or hereafter installed, shall be equipped with an approved water conserving device. Ice cubers and ice flakers shall be excepted when approved by the Commissioner as to method of installation.

R-2. All refrigeration systems using City water without an approved water conserving device shall be equipped with an automatic water regulating valve or device on each individual unit comprising the installation.

R-3. Where the refrigeration unit using City water is one-third (⅓) ton of rated capacity or less, and the unit is located in a metered premise, then the unit shall be connected to the metered supply.

Pertaining to Air Conditioning:

AC-1. All air conditioning systems in excess of two (2) tons of rated capacity using City water, heretofore or hereafter installed, shall be equipped with an approved water conserving device.

AC-2. All air conditioning sytsems using City water without an approved water conserving device shall be equipped with an automatic water regulating valve or device on each individual unit.

The Division of Air Conditioning has been established for receiving and reviewing requests for variances from this directive due to peculiar individual situations.

Infractions of Rules 177A, 177B and 177C shall be punishable by a fine as provided for in Chapter 30 Section 734 (4)-4.0 of the Administrative Code and/or by closing and sealing of the City water supply valve to the unit or units.

RULE 177D

RULES GOVERNING HOURS OF USE OF AIR CONDITIONING SYSTEMS

(As amended and filed with the City Clerk on [July 11, 1966).

1. Hours of use of Air Conditioning systems may be promulgated from time to time, as water supply conditions so warrant.

2. Lists of "permissible hourly operation" will be on file in the Department and can be obtainable upon request.

3. It is further directed that the hours during which air conditioning using City water shall be posted prominently in each building and establishment using such air conditioning. Official operating Time Cards may be obtainable from the Department, upon request.

4. When such hours are in effect, infractions shall be punishable by a fine as provided for in Chapter 30, Section 734 (4)-4.0 of the Administrative Code, and/or the closing and sealing of the City water supply valve or valves to the system.

5. The Division of Air Conditioning has been established for receiving and reviewing requests for variances from this directive due to unique individual situations.

6. It should be noted that this directive applies only to air conditioning using City water and does not apply to air conditioning using private well water, nor does it apply to air cooled air conditioners.

Service Check Valve.   178. A check valve shall be placed in all services where the following conditions exist:
(1) Where a building is supplied by services connected to different mains.

(2) Where there is any possibility of backflow from tanks, siamese connections or other apparatus or fixtures within the building. The check valves shall be placed within 2 feet of the outlet side of the main house control valve and on metered connections between the meter test tee and the outlet valve.

(3) Where there is a possibility of contamination at well swing connection to City water supply when used in emergencies. See sketch below, Sec. 141.09 (F).

SEC. 141.09 (F)
SWING JOINT CONNECTION BETWEEN CITY WATER AND WELL WATER SUPPLY

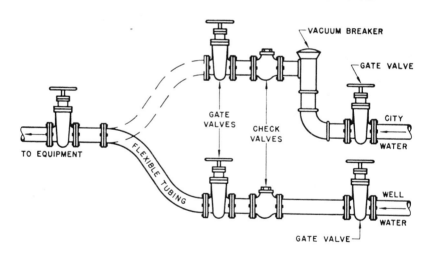

Hot Water Check.   179. Water supply lines to hot water boilers, steam boilers or similar fixtures or apparatus through which there might occur a backflow of hot water or steam, shall be equipped with a check valve, on the outlet side of which a relief valve shall be installed.

Water Hammer Arrester.   180. Where flushometers, suction tanks, other fixtures or piping, are equipped with quick closing valves and are supplied by direct street pressure in excess of 70 pounds, a water hammer arrester (approved type) shall be installed within two feet of the house control valve or meter in the service near the point of entry. Where water hammer conditions exist in any installation, regardless of the pressure obtaining, an air chamber of an approved type (see sketch below) shall be installed where and as directed by the Department.

APPROVED AIR-CHAMBER

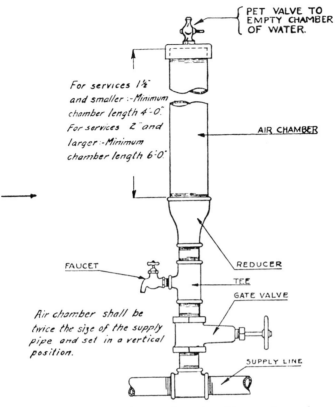

PET VALVE TO EMPTY CHAMBER OF WATER.

For services 1½" and smaller :-Minimum chamber length 4'-0".
For services 2" and larger :-Minimum chamber length 6'-0".

AIR CHAMBER

FAUCET

REDUCER

TEE

GATE VALVE

Air chamber shall be twice the size of the supply pipe and set in a vertical position.

SUPPLY LINE

Pumped Supply. 181A. A pumped supply, with a total capacity exceeding 400 gallons per minute, shall not be connected directly to the City main.

For installations of larger capacities, plans must be submitted for the approval of the Engineer in charge of the Bureau of Water Supply in the borough.

This regulation will not apply to fire pumps, except where the size of the fire service is equal to or greater than the size of the street main.

Suction Tank. 181B. When the pumps cannot be connected directly to the water service main a suction (surge) tank shall be installed.

Suction tanks shall be constructed in accordance with the requirements for a gravity house tank.

Suction tanks shall have a capacity not less than the following listing:

TABLE

Total Connect Pump Capacity in G. P. M.	Tank Capacity in Gallons
0-100	1000
101-200	3000
201-350	5000
351-500	7500
501 and over	10000

Low Pressure Cut-Off Required on Booster Pumps.

181C. When a booster pump is used on a water pressure booster system there shall be installed a low pressure cut-off on the booster pump suction to prevent the creation of a pressure on the suction side of the pump less than 10 psi below the normal static street pressure, at the point of entry of the water service.

Check Valves Required.

181D. Each pump discharge shall be provided with a check valve and gate valve.

Hydrant Flow Test.

182. A hydrant flow test to determine the residual pressure at a certain volume will be made at a designated point upon payment of $25.00.

Use of Fire Hydrant.

183. Hydrants are to be used only by authorized employees of this Department, of the Fire Department, or by persons holding a permit from this Department. The water obtained from hydrants by persons holding a permit from this Department shall be used only for the purpose stated on the permit and in such a manner as to prevent all waste.

Connection with fire hydrants shall be made by valve and couplings which can be readily detached in case of emergency. Where valve and couplings are used the hydrant must be opened full at all times and the rate of flow shall be governed by the installed valve, and all such connections shall be uncoupled immediately after use. Hose connected to hydrant shall be equipped with an automatic shut off device to prevent waste.

Hydrants shall be protected from freezing at all times and hydrants used during the period from November 1st to April 15th shall be pumped out immediately after use. No hydrant is to be used when the temperature is below 35 degrees Fahrenheit.

Only hydrant wrenches of a design approved by the Department shall be used. Water shall be obtained from the small size nozzle; the cap on the larger nozzle shall not be disturbed. Care shall be taken that the cap chains are not broken or caps lost; and the cap shall be replaced securely after use of hydrant. No high pressure fire hydrant shall be opened.

No hydrant shall be used which appears to be in a defective condition and if a hydrant is in a defective condition, the Department shall be notified immediately giving the location thereof.

Fire hydrants are not to be obstructed by the users thereof, and shall be available at all times for use by the Fire Department.

The permittee agrees to pay for all water used in connection with the permit at the established rate.

If damage to a hydrant results from use thereof, repairs shall be made at the expense of the user.

The person or company to whom a permit is issued shall indemnify and hold the City of New York harmless from all liability or damage of whatever nature by reason of the opening of said hydrants or the use of water therefrom by said person, his agent, servants or employees.

The permit may be cancelled, and no further permits issued to a permittee, if any of the conditions herein mentioned are violated and for such other reasons as the Commissioner may consider adequate.

A summons will be served on any person operating a fire hydrant unless he has received written permission from the Commissioner of this Department or his duly designated representative.

THE PERMIT MUST BE RETAINED AT THE POINT WHERE WATER IS BEING USED.

(See Sec. 734(1)-5.0 of the Administrative Code.)

Use of Water Restricted. 184. The use of the pressure or flow of water from the City system as a source of energy is prohibited except when specifically approved by the Department.

The use of water is permitted subject to such conditions or reservations as the Department may consider reasonable.

The Department reserves the right to restrict or prohibit extraordinary use of water if water supply conditions so require.

The use of City water for coolant purposes in industrial and commercial equipment is prohibited except where an approved conserving device as defined in Rule 177A, paragraph I, is used, or an automatic flow regulating device such as a solenoid valve which permits flow only during operation or a thermal valve which regulates the flow to temperature requirements, or a similar apparatus which limits the flow during operation to manufacturer's requirements is installed on each unit of equipment.

This rule shall become effective as of January 1, 1967.

Use of Water. 185. Display fountains, ornamental pools, aquarium, etc., using water in excess of the rate of ½ G.P.M. shall be recirculated.

Miscellaneous Fixtures to Be Metered. 186. Outdoor irrigation system, swimming pools, wading pool, or other commercial device requiring for its operation the use of City water, shall not be installed or used except where the supply of water to the fixture or device is metered.

Hose Bib or Outside Water Connection. 187. The use of a hose bib or other outside hose connection for garden purposes, for watering lawns or for flushing a sidewalk, stoop or areaway, is restricted to such use and to the period of each year as prescribed by Rule 34 of the Rules and Regulations Fixing Uniform Annual Charges and Extra and Miscellaneous Charges for the supply of water.

Ownership of Taps, Services, Meters and Appurtenances. 188. Installation and maintenance of taps (corporation stops; wet connection sleeves, and valves three-ways, etc.) service pipes, curb stops, meters and appurtenances shall be entirely at the expense of the owner.

Access by. 189. Officers, agents and employees of this Department shall, in their official capacity, have free access at proper and reasonable hours to all parts of every building, boat or place in which meters are located and where City water is or may be furnished or used.

Shutting Off Supply for Inspection Purposes. 190. A Department employee or agent, when authorized, may shut off the water supply for the purpose of inspection or to make repairs or alterations to water mains, meters, pipes, valves or other appurtenances. No other person shall open, close or tamper with any valve, valve box or valve box cover, or any other equipment in a city main.

Shut-Off Charges. 191. When it is necessary for the Department to shut off a tap because of a leaking service, non-payment of a bill, or non-compliance with the Department regulations, the owner will be charged with all costs incidental thereto.

Prevention of Waste. 192. All owners, occupants or lessees obtaining water from the City system will be obliged to prevent leakage or waste of such water under penalty of fine prescribed under the provisions of the Administrative Code, Section 734(4)-4.0-4.1-4.2.

Deviation from Rules. 193. If unusual subsurface or other conditions make it impractical in the opinion of the Department, to complete any installation in conformity with these rules and regulations, the work may be performed in such manner as directed.

Violations.   194. In case of violation of any of the preceding rules and regulations, or any of the laws of statutes relating to water supply, or if it shall be found that a meter has been tampered with, the water supply will be shut off unless such additional charges as the Commissioner may impose are paid promptly, nor will the supply be reestablished except upon correction of the violation in conformity with Department rules and upon payment of the expense of shutting off and turning on the water supply. Satisfactory assurance shall also be given that there will be no future cause for complaint.

Acting under authority of Paragraph 3, Section 734, Chapter 30 of the New York City Charter, I hereby establish, effective immediately, rules and regulations as set forth herein.

Dated May 20, 1966.

ROBERT D. CLARK, Acting Commissioner,
Department of Water Supply, Gas and Electricity.

APPENDIX

TABLES TO BE USED TO DETERMINE THE SIZE OF SERVICE PIPES AND TAPS

The following tables numbered 1, 2, 3, and 4 are to be used to determine the size of service pipe and taps as stated in Rule No. 138, Revised July 1, 1962, of the "Rules and Regulations Governing and Restricting Use and Supply of Water in New York City."

Table No. 1 lists "Fixture Units" which are to be used to determine the water demand load of the premises. Based on the usage and the type of valve, various plumbing fixtures are assigned fixture unit values.

Table No. 2 tabulates the "Maximum Probable Demand," in gallons per minute, corresponding to the total number of "Fixture Units" as determined from Table No. 1. Fixture Units are tabulated in two columns. The first column is to be used for premises where more than 20% of the toilets have flush valves (flushometers), while the second is for premises where 20% or less of the toilets have flush valves.

Table No. 3 or Table No. 4 give the "Size of Service Pipe and Taps" for different lengths of service pipe and rates of flow. Table No. 3 is for general use. Under certain conditions, Table No. 4 may be used for 1-, 2-, 3-, and 4-family dwellings. In addition, the use of 1-inch service pipe for one-family dwellings is permitted for specified conditions.

How to Use The Tables

Step 1. To determine the total number of "Fixture Units" of the premises use Table No. 1. For each type of fixture find the equivalent value in "Fixture Units" based on the usage and type of valve. Calculate the total number of "Fixture Units."

Step 2a. Using Table No. 2, convert the total number of "Fixture Units" to the corresponding rate of flow, in gallons per minute, for the maximum probable demand (mpd).

2b. Add the maximum rate of flow (gpm), for all fixtures or units with constant demands, to the maximum probable demand as determined in Step 2a.

2c. If the premises are to be supplied by pumping to a roof or other tank, the maximum capacity of the pump or pumps shall be considered the maximum probable demand.

Step 3. To determine the size of service pipe and taps for the premises, use Table No. 3, Table No. 4, or the special allowance for one-family dwellings. In the column for the appropriate length of service pipe, find the rate of flow equal to or larger than the value determined in Step 2. Corresponding to this rate of flow, read at the left the size of service pipe and tap required for the premises.

GOOSENECK SHALL BE SIZED THE SAME AS THE SERVICE PIPE.

Table No. 1. Fixture Units–Table of Equivalents

FIXTURE	DWELLINGS	COMMERCIAL, INDUSTRIAL AND PUBLIC BUILDINGS
Kitchen and Laundry		
Kitchen Sink	2	4
Laundry Tray		
(1 to 3 sections)	3	3
Dish Washer		
(½-in. outlet)	1	4
Washing Machine		
(Automatic)	2	*
Bathroom, Washroom & Shower		
Bathroom Group (Toilet, Basin,		
Bathtub or Shower)		
− Tank	6	...
− Flush Valve	8	...
Toilet-Tank	3	5
− Flush Valve	6	10
Wash Basin	1	2
**Bathtub	2	4
**Shower	2	4
Urinal, stall or wall		
− Tank	...	3
− Flush Valve	3	5
Urinal, pedestal		
−Flush Valve	...	10
Plumbing Outlets to Fixtures Other Than Above		
½ inch and smaller	1	2
¾ inch	2	4
1 inch	3	6

*The number of Fixture Units for a Washing Machine in a Commercial, Industrial, or Public Building is determined by the size of its plumbing outlet.

**A Bathtub and a Shower over it are considered together as only one fixture.

Table No. 2. Probable Maximum Demand

Fixture Units**		Rate of Flow*
For premises where the percentage of toilets having flush valves (flushometers) is: a) more than 20%	b) 20% or less	(gallons per minute) for corresponding fixture units.
...	10	8
...	15	12
...	20	15
5	30	20
10	40	25
15	60	33
25	80	39
35	100	43
50	125	49
65	150	55
75	175	60
90	200	64
100	210	66
110	225	70
125	250	74
150	270	78
175	300	83
200	340	92
250	375	100
300	410	105
325	450	115
350	475	120
400	500	130
450	550	135
500	600	140
550	630	150
600	700	155
650	720	165
700	750	170
750	800	180
800	850	185
850	875	190
900	925	195
950	950	200
1000	1000	205
1500	1500	270
2000	2000	330
2500	2500	380
3000	3000	440
3500	3500	490
4000	4000	540
5000	5000	670

*To determine rates of flow corresponding to fixture units above 5000, add 100 gallons per minute for each additional thousand fixture units, to the figure of 670 gallons per minute (the flow corresponding to 5000 fixture units).

**Interpolate to determine the rate of flow (gpm) corresponding to fixture units that have values *between* the values listed.

Example: 265 fixture units, in column b, falls between 250 and 270

250 – 74
265 – unknown 'x' $\frac{15}{20} = \frac{x}{4}$ x = 3; 74 + 3 = 77 gpm
270 – 78

Table No. 3. Size of Service Pipe and Taps
Dwellings, Commercial, Industrial and Public Buildings

**(Based on the Rate of Flow in gallons per minute
and the Length of Service Pipe in feet.)**

House Service	Tap or Wet Conn.	10	20	25	30	40	50	55	60	80	100
SIZE, in inches		LENGTH OF SERVICE PIPE, in feet									
1	¾	21	15	13	12	10	9	9	8	7	6
1¼	1	37	25	23	21	17	16	15	14	13	12
1½	1	55	41	37	34	28	25	24	23	20	18
2	1½	100	84	75	70	59	52	50	48	41	37
2½	2	150	150	135	125	105	93	90	86	73	65
3	3	220	220	210	200	165	145	140	135	120	105
3½	3	300	300	300	290	250	220	210	200	170	155
4	3	390	390	390	390	350	320	305	290	250	220
5	4	600	600	600	600	600	550	525	500	430	380
6	6	880	880	880	880	880	880	840	810	700	620
8	6	1550	1550	1550	1550	1550	1550	1550	1550	1400	1300
10	8	2450	2450	2450	2450	2450	2450	2450	2450	2450	2300
12	10	3500	3500	3500	3500	3500	3500	3500	3500	3500	3500

Note.—The flows in the above Table No. 3 are based on a maximum pressure loss of 2 lbs. per square inch in the Service Pipe or a maximum velocity of 10 ft. per sec., whichever gives the smaller rate of flow. (See Note Below.)

Table No. 4. 1-, 2-, 3-, and 4-family Dwellings

**(RESTRICTED TO 1-, 2-, 3-, and 4-family dwellings located on a street
with at least 40 lbs. per square inch pressure and where
the highest ceiling is not more than 30 feet above the street level.)**

Service	Tap	10	20	25	30	40	50	55	60	80	100
SIZE, in inches		LENGTH OF SERVICE PIPE, in feet									
1	¾	24	24	23	21	18	17	16	15	13	12
1¼	1	38	38	38	36	31	28	26	25	22	19
1½	1	55	55	55	55	50	45	43	41	35	31

The flows in Table No. 4 are based on a maximum pressure loss of 6 lbs. per square inch in the Service Pipe, or a maximum velocity of 10 ft. per sec., whichever gives the smaller rate of flow. (See Note Below.)

HOWEVER, for One (1) Family Dwellings, without flush valves, where the street pressure is at least 40 lbs. per square inch, the following maximum lengths of 1-inch Service Pipes will be allowed for the rates of flow indicated. This permits the use of a 1-inch Service Pipe and ¾-inch Tap.

55 feet for not more than 18 gallons per minute.
80 feet for not more than 15 gallons per minute.
100 feet for not more than 13 gallons per minute.

Note.—In Table No. 3 and Table No. 4, flows above the horizontal lines are limited by the allowable maximum pressure loss, and those below the line, by the allowable maximum velocity.

EXAMPLES TO ILLUSTRATE HOW TO DETERMINE
THE SIZES OF TAPS AND SERVICES

Example 1. A 20-family apartment building on a 60-ft.-wide street where the main is on the far side. Each apartment shall have a bathroom group, with tank type toilets, and kitchen sink. A washing machine with permanent or semi-permanent connections to the plumbing system will be located on the premises, also two ½-inch hose bibs.

Computations:

a. 20 bathroom groups (tank type) x 6 = 120
   20 kitchen sinks   x 2 = 40
   1 washing machine   x 2 =   2
   2 hose bibs   x 1 =   2
   Total Fixture Units (F.U.)   = 164

b. From Table No. 2 column b,   164 F.U. = 58 gpm.

c. The length of service is approximately 2' + 13' + 25' = 40 ft.

d. In Table No. 3 under the column for 40 ft., find the value in gpm equal to or just larger than 58 gpm. Such an amount is 59 gpm. At the left we find that to satisfy this condition requires a 2-inch service pipe and 1½-inch tap.

Example 2. A 100-family apartment building, where 25 apartments have 2 bathroom groups apiece and 75 have only one apiece. Each apartment has a kitchen sink. Located on the premises are 5 laundry rooms with 3 washing machines in each. There are also five ½-inch hose bibs.

Computations:

a. 25 double bathroom groups (tank) 2 x 6 = 300
   75 single bathroom groups (tank)   x 6 = 450
   100 sinks   x 2 = 200
   5 x 3 washing machines   x 2 = 30
   5 hose bibs   x 1 =   5
   Total Fixture Units   985

b. From Table 2 Column b 1, 985 F.U. = 204 gpm.

c. Length of service (main on near side) = approx. 25 ft.

d. Table No. 3, column 25 ft.–210 gpm. requires a 3-inch service pipe and a 3-inch wet connection.

Example 3. A three-family house that contains the fixtures given below and the highest ceiling is 27 ft. above the street level, is located on a street where the pressure is 40 psi. The street is 80 ft. wide and the main is located on the far side.

Computations:

a. 3 bathroom groups (tank) x 6 = 18
   3 kitchen sinks   x 2 = 6
   3 dishwashers   x 1 = 3
   2 washing machines   x 2 = 4
   1 laundry tray   x 3 = 3
   2 hose bibs   x 1 = <u>2</u>
   Total Fixture Units   = 36

b. Rate of Flow = 23 gpm.

c. Length of service. 2′ + 18′ + 35′ = 55 ft.

d. In Table No. 4, column for 55 ft. 26 gpm is just larger than 23 gpm. For this condition a 1¼-inch service pipe and a 1-inch tap is required.

Example 4. A one-family house with a 50 ft. service is located on a street where the pressure is 40 lbs. per sq. inch and has the following fixtures:

Computations:

a. 1 Laundry tray   x 3 = 3
   2 bathroom groups (tank) x 6 = 12
   1 toilet   x 3 = 3
   1 basin   x 1 = 1
   1 kitchen sink   x 2 = 2
   1 dishwasher   x 1 = 1
   1 washing machine   x 2 = 2
   2 hose bibs   x 1 = <u>2</u>
   Total Fixture Units   = 26

b. Rate of Flow = 18 gpm.

Since it is a one-family house, located on a street where the pressure is 40 psi, the length of service pipe less than 55 feet, the rate of flow 18 gpm., a 1-inch service pipe and a ¾-inch tap can, therefore, be used.

HOW TO DETERMINE WATER PIPE PRESSURE REQUIRED

Step 1.   From the Department of Water Supply, Gas and Electricity, obtain the information on "minimum pressure in street water main at peak load (about 6:00 P.M.)."

Step 2a. Determine the height in feet of the uppermost fixture above the street water main. (Use 68 feet in this case.)

2b.   Multiply by .434 to convert height, in feet, to psi.

2c.   Add 15 psi water pressure required at top floor if flushometers are used.

Add 8 psi water pressure required at top floor if toilet tanks are used. In some cases a higher pressure is required.

Step 3.   Addition of Step 2b and 2c equals the total pressure required.

Step 4.   Available pressure for friction loss

$$\frac{\text{in psi} \times 100'}{\text{Length of pipe, in feet, to furthest fixture}} = \text{Psi pressure allowable for friction loss per } 100' \text{ of pipe}$$

NOTE. If required psi cannot be maintained at upper floors at all times, use method as per Section P107.7 of the BUILDING CODE, such as a gravity or pressure tank, etc., to supply the required amount of water to those floors.

Example

Step 1.   On information from the Department of Water Supply, Gas and Electricity, the minimum street pressure is 65 psi.

Step 2.

2a and 2b   68' X .434 equals   29.5 psi
2c   plus   15. psi required at top floor
                                        (Flushometers being used)

Step 3.   Total pressure required = 44.5 psi (Not including friction loss)

Step 4.   Minimum pressure in street water main   65 psi (See Step 1)
Less (Total pressure required)   44.5 psi (See Step 3)
                                            = 19.5 psi (Pressure available
                                                      for friction loss)

$$\text{Using } \frac{19.5 \text{ psi} \times 100'}{190' \text{ to uppermost fixture}} = \text{10.3 psi available for friction loss per 100 feet of pipe}$$

NOTE. Allowance to be made in equivalent length of pipe for friction loss in valves and fittings. Also add allowance for friction loss for other items such as water meters, filters, etc. The above figure of 190' in the example can be the actual measured length of pipe, plus the allowance for the fittings, etc.

HOW TO DETERMINE WATER DISTRIBUTION PIPE SIZE FOR BRANCHES, RISERS, and MAINS

FOR HOT WATER BRANCHES AND RISERS.–

Figure 75% of Fixture Units for the fixtures that use hot <u>and</u> cold water.

FOR COLD WATER BRANCHES AND RISERS.–

Figure 75% of Fixture Units for the fixtures that use hot <u>and</u> cold water. Figure 100% of Fixture Units for the fixtures that use <u>cold</u> water <u>only</u>. Risers may be reduced in the direction of the last branch.

FOR MAINS AND BRANCH MAINS.–

To be sized by using the Fixture Unit values of the <u>fixtures</u> using hot and/or cold water.

Example: <u>FOR BRANCHES AND RISERS.–</u>

Fixtures using 100 fixture units of <u>hot and cold water.</u>–
   (For hot water supply piping)   100 F.U. $\times$ .75 = 75 F.U.
   (For cold water supply piping)   100 F.U. $\times$ .75 = 75 F.U.
Fixtures using 100 fixture units of <u>cold water only</u> = 100 F.U.

<u>FOR MAINS AND BRANCH MAINS.–</u>

Using 100 F.U. (Hot and cold water fixtures)   = 100 F.U.
Using 100 F.U. (Cold water fixtures only)   = <u>100 F.U.</u>
Total = 200 F.U.

The required size of the <u>Water Distribution</u> pipes within a building may be determined in sections.

METHOD OF DETERMINING AMOUNT OF FIXTURE UNITS BEING SUPPLIED BY WATER SUPPLY PIPING

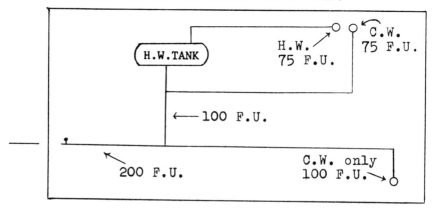

For COMPUTATION of PIPE SIZES use CHARTS 1, and 2 or 3 as mentioned in Steps Nos. 1, 2, and 3.

Step 1. Determine the amount of Fixture Units that a branch, riser, or main is required to supply with water.

Step 2. Use CHART No. 1 to convert Fixture Units to gpm.

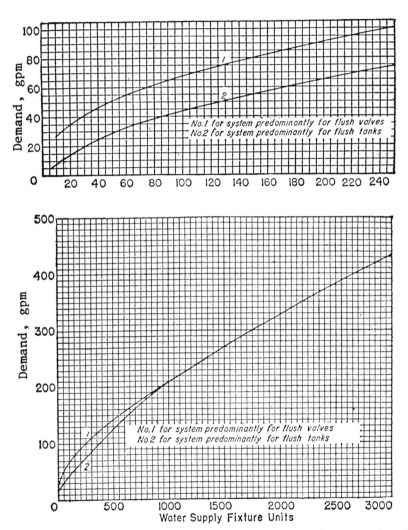

Chart No. 1. (Top) Curves for estimating demand load (at enlarged scale); (Bottom) Curves for estimating demand load.

NOTE. FIGURES IN CHART No. 1 COMPARE WITH "TABLES TO BE USED TO DETERMINE THE SIZE OF SERVICE PIPES AND TAPS"

Step 3. After determining the amount of gpm required, use CHART No. 2 if "Brass or Copper" piping is to be used, and CHART No. 3 if "Galvanized Steel or Wrought Iron" piping is to be used.

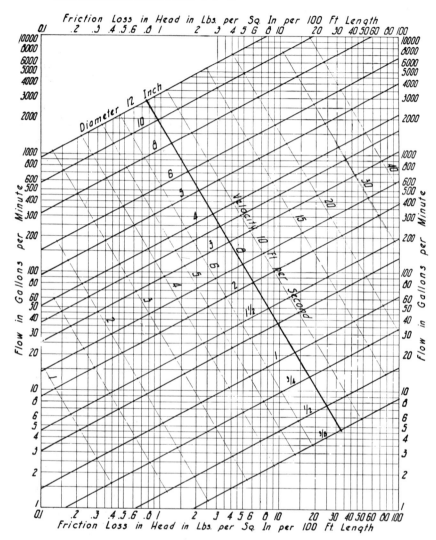

Chart No. 2. Flow Chart for fairly smooth pipe (brass and copper).

NOTE.—When using CHART No. 2 or CHART No. 3, the average permissible FRICTION LOSS and the estimated MAXIMUM LOAD must be known.

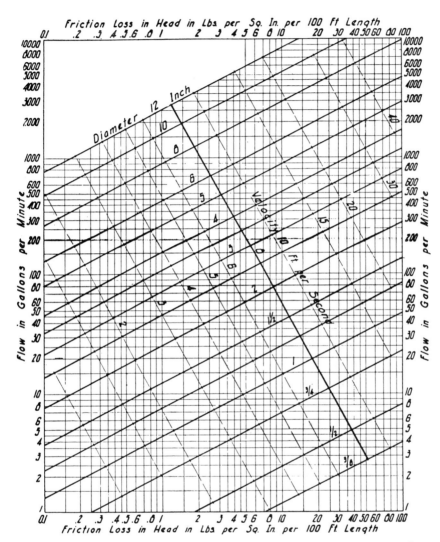

Chart No. 3. Flow Chart for Fairly Rough Pipe. (Galvanized Steel and Wrought Iron).

MAXIMUM VELOCITY NOT TO EXCEED 8 fps as per SECTION
P107.5(e)(2) OF THE BUILDING CODE.

Allowance in Equivalent Lengths of Pipe for
Friction Loss for Valves and Threaded Fittings

Nominal Diameters, (inches)	90° Ell	45° Ell	Tee	Coupling	Gate Valve	Globe Valve	Angle Valve
	Equivalent Length of Pipe (feet)						
$^3/_8$	1	0.6	1.5	0.3	0.2	8	4
$^1/_2$	2	1.2	3	.6	.4	15	8
$^3/_4$	2.5	1.5	4	.8	.5	20	12
1	3	1.8	5	.9	.6	25	15
$1^1/_4$	4	2.4	6	1.2	.8	35	18
$1^1/_2$	5	3	7	1.5	1.0	45	22
2	7	4	10	2	1.3	55	28
$2^1/_2$	8	5	12	2.5	1.6	65	34
3	10	6	15	3	2.0	80	40
$3^1/_2$	12	7	18	3.6	2.4	100	50
4	14	8	21	4.0	2.7	125	55
5	17	10	25	5	3.3	140	70
6	20	12	30	6	4.0	165	80

FORMULAS

PI or π = 3.1416 or $\frac{22}{7}$.

Diameter PI = Circumference.

Circumference $\div PI$ = Diameter.

$PI\ R^2$ = Area of a circle-------Base $\times$ height $\div$ 2 = Area of a triangle.

$\frac{PI}{4} \times D^2$ = Area of a circle.

$D^2 \times .7854$ = Area of a circle.

$D^2 \times .7854 \times H$ = Volume of a cylindrical tank.

Area of a base $\times$ height = Volume of a cylinder.

Base $\times$ height = Area of a rectangle.

Length $\times$ width = Area of a square rectangle.

Length $\times$ width $\times$ height = Volume of a square or a rectangle.

$D^3 \times .5236$ = Volume of a sphere or $V = \dfrac{3.1416 \times D^3}{6}$.

$D^3 \times .2618$ = Volume of a hemisphere.

$.7854 \times D \times d$ = Area of an ellipse.

$D^{2''} \times .0034 \times H''$ = Gals. of water in a cylindrical tank. (Height and diameter must be in inches.)

$D^{2''} \times .0408 \times H'$ = Gals. of water in a cylindrical tank or pipe. (Height must be in feet; diameter, in inches.)

$D^{2''} \times .7854 \times H'' \div 231$ = Gals. of water in a cylindrical tank. (Height and diameter must be in inches.)

FORMULAS AND EQUIVALENTS

1. Atmospheric Pressure = 14.7 lbs. per sq. in.
2. Atmospheric Pressure = 33.8 ft. of water per sq. in.
3. Atmospheric Pressure = 30 inches of mercury per sq. in.
4. Weight of 1 cubic inch of water = .03617 lbs.
5. Weight of 1 cubic inch of mercury = .49 lbs.
6. Specific Gravity of mercury = 13.6
7. Weight of 1 cubic foot of water = 62.5 pounds
8. Weight of 1 U.S. gallon of water = 8.35 pounds
9. 1 cubic foot of water = 7.5 (7.48) gallons
10. 1 U.S. gallon of water = 231 cubic inches
11. Pressure at the bottom of a column of one foot of water = .434 lb. per sq. in.
12. Pressure at the bottom of a column of water 2.31 feet or 27.7 inches = 1 lb. pressure per sq. in.
13. To find pressure = Height (Head) $\times$ .434 for each foot high
14. To find Head (height) that water will rise = Pressure $\times$ 2.31
15. 32°F (Fahrenheit) = freezing of fresh water
16. 27°F (Fahrenheit) = freezing of salt water
17. $c = \sqrt{a^2 + b^2}$
    $a = \sqrt{c^2 - b^2}$
    $b = \sqrt{c^2 - a^2}$ 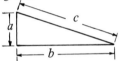   RIGHT TRIANGLE

18. To find the diameter of a circle that is equivalent to two given circles:
$$D = \sqrt{d^2 - d^2}$$
$$D^2 = \sqrt{d^2 + d^2}$$

19. Formula for the ratio of pipe capacities: R varies as $\sqrt{\left(\dfrac{D}{d}\right)^5}$

     R = Number of smaller pipes the larger one will supply
     D = Diameter of larger pipe
     d = Diameter of smaller pipes

Example:
     How many 2-inch pipes will a 4-inch pipe supply?

$$R = \sqrt{\left(\frac{4}{2}\right)^5} = \sqrt{(2)^5} = \sqrt{32} = 5.657 \; Answer$$

HOUSING AND DEVELOPMENT ADMINISTRATION
DEPARTMENT OF BUILDINGS

DIRECTIVE NUMBER 24-1970

TO: Borough Superintendents

FROM: John T. O'Neill
          Commissioner

Date: June 25, 1970

Subject: Availability of Public
              Sewers-Section C26-1600.6,
              Administrative Code.

Sub-division (e) of Section C26-1600.6 of the Administrative Code requires that the drainage system of any building, structure, premises or part thereof be connected to a public sewer system, if available.

Sub-section (2) of this sub-division indicates that a public sewer system shall be deemed available to a one and two family dwelling if a property line of such dwelling is within 100 feet of the public sewer system; and, that a public sewer system shall be deemed available to all other buildings if a property line of such building is within 500 feet of the public sewer system.

Sub-section (2) of this sub-division further prescribes that where 2 or more private dwellings are to be constructed on a tract of land, or where a substantial improvement of other type of building or buildings are contemplated on a tract of land, the public sewer systems may be declared available by the agencies having jurisdiction, even though the above-mentioned distances are exceeded.

Hereafter, whenever the Department of Water Resources indicates on sewer information forms that a public sewer is available, the Borough Office is to require that the drainage system of any building or premises be connected thereto, regardless of the distance to the public sewer, with the exception of a single private dwelling.

The design of the sanitary and storm sewerage systems on private property shall be in conformance with the Building Code. The design of the private sewers in the streets, whether or not the streets are city owned, shall be in conformance with the requirements of the Department of Water Resources, and shall be referred to that agency for approval. No permit shall be issued unless approved plans by all agencies having jurisdiction have been submitted.

Discharge of storm water onto flat areas such as driveways, as may be permitted for one or two family dwellings pursuant to section P110.2 of Reference Standard RS-16, shall be authorized only in the case of a single private dwelling.

This directive is to take effect immediately.

John T. O'Neill
Commissioner

JTO:IEM:ap
cc: Executive Staff
      The Industry

      Dr. Costello-Dep. Mayor-City Administrator
      Commr. Feldman, Dept. of Water Resources

INDEX
BUILDING CODE–CITY OF NEW YORK
All references are to SUB-ARTICLE or Section numbers.
("C26-" is omitted from Section numbers in this index.)

Abandoned operations, see Discontinued operations
Absorption tests, masonry, 3.2.1(b) (RS10-1)
Academies, Occupancy Classification, 302.1
Acceptance requirements, construction materials, see Construction materials, acceptance requirements
Acceptance tests, boilers, 1401.1(a)
elevators, 1802.1
Accessory additions, 101.1
Accessory buildings, Inside Fire Districts, 403.2(c)
Access panels, 401.2(a), 401.2(c)
Access stairs, 604.8(1) (2)
Adjoining buildings, protection of, 1902.1(d)
Adjoining properties, caissons, 1112.6
cofferdams, 1112.6
construction required, 1112.6
excavations, 1112.6, 1902.3
filling operations, 1902.3
foundation operations, 1902.4
inspection, 1902.1(b)
license to enter, 1902.1(a)
physical examination, 1902.1(b)
protection of, 1902.0
underpinning, 1112.6
Adjoining structures, 1903.1(b)
frost protection, 1903.1(b)(1)c
license to enter, 1903.1(b)(1)
protection of, 1905.2
Adjoining walls, protection of, 1902.1(c)
Admixtures, 1004.6
Adsorption devices, mechanical ventilation, 1206.4
Air blower systems, construction, 1300.7(e)
Airborne noise, 1208.2(a)
Air-conditioned rooms, 1207.9(a)
Air conditioning systems, 1206.3(b), 1300.1
city water, use of, 1300.7(g), 1304.4
construction, 1300.7(a)
installation, 1206.5
operation, 1206.5
permits, 1300.1
plans, 1300.1

Air cooling, 1300.1
permits, 1300.1
plans, 1300.1
Air hammers, 1107.1(c)(1)
Air heating, 1300.1
permits, 1300.1
plans, 1300.1
Air Pollution Control Code, 1901.3(a)
Air supply, 1408.1
gas fuels, 1408.1(b)
oil fuels, 1408.1(a)
solid fuels, 1408.(1)(c)
Air-supported structures, 719.0, 800.3
blowers for, 719.7(a)
certificate of occupancy, 719.8
construction, 719.5(b)
flame resistance, 719.6(b)
heat for, 719.7(a)
height, 719.1
location, 719.1
pressurization system, 719.7
separations, 719.2
Aisles, assembly spaces, 801.8
capacity, 801.8(a)(i)
lighting, 801.8(a)(9)
steps, 801.8(a)(7)
tapered, 801.8(a)(3)
uniform, 801.8(a)(4)
width, 801.8(a)(2)
Alarm systems, fire, see Fire Alarm systems
sprinkler systems, 1703.4, see also Sprinkler systems
Alcoves, natural ventilation, 1205.3
Alterations, 1800.11, 1900.1, 1906.0
barricades, 1906.1
of building value, 103.5
cost, 103.5
dumbwaiters, 1800.11
escalators, 1800.11
exceeding 60 per cent of building value, 103.1
minor building code, 104.1, 104.3
multi-family dwellings, 1201.1
occupancy change, 103.4
permits, 109.2(b)

signs, 1906.1
under 30 per cent of building value, 103.3
use, change in, 103.4
Aluminum, identification, 1007.2
  inspection requirements, Table 10-1
  inspection requirements, Table 10-2
  quality control, 1007.3
  structural design, 1007.0
  welding operations, 1007.3(b)
Amusement parks, 803.1(e)
Anchors, masonry, 3.3 (RS10-1), 9 (RS10-1)
Anesthetic agents, storage, 701.6
Antenna supports, combustible construction,
  503.8(j)
Apartment houses, Occupancy Classification,
  302.1
Arches, flat, 12.1 (RS10-1)
  Inside Fire Districts, 403.2(f)
Areas of refuse, doors, locking, 604.5(d)
  exits, 604.5(c)
  floor area, 604.5(b)
  separation, 604.5(a)
Artificial lighting, see Lighting, artificial
Ash storage pits, 704.5
  boiler rooms, 704.5
Assemblies, controlled inspection, Table 10-1
Assembly, places of; see Places of assembly
Assembly, classification
  Occupancy group F
  places of assembly, 307.1
Assembly Occupancy Classification, see Occupancy Classification, assembly
Assembly rooms, ventilation, 1207.9(c)
Assembly spaces, aisles, 801.8
  bench seating, 801.7(a)(4)
  bleacher seating, 801.7(a)(2)
    aisles, 801.7(2)c.
  box, 801.7(a)(1)
  chair seating, 801.7(a)(1)
  collecting, 801.11(a)(1)
  counter seating, 801.7(a)(6)
  cross aisles, 801.8
  dimensions, 801.1.11(a)(3)
  directional signs, 801.17
    exit, 801.10(e)
  doors, 801.11(a)(7)
  emergency lighting, 801.18
  exit doors, 801.10(f)
  exit openings, 801.10
    capacity, 801.10(a)
    classification, 801.10(c)

distribution, 801.10(d)
  location, 801.10(e)
  width, 801.10(b)
exit signs, 801.17
exits, 801.11(a)(6)
lighting, 801.16(a)
loge, 801.7(a)(1)
movable chairs, 801.7(a)(1)
normal entry, 801.10, 801.10(c)
occupancy classification, 302.1, 307.0
occupied load, 801.11(a)(2)
pew seating, 801.7(a)(4)
platform seating, 801.7(a)(3)
posted capacity, 801.3
protective guards, 801.7(a)(8)
ramps, 801.61(a)(5)
seating plans, 801.4(a)
standee areas, 801.7(a)(7)
table and chair seating, 801.7(a)(5)
travel distance, 801.9
vomitories, 801.8(b)(10)
Assembly structures, moving live loads,
  902.7(i)
Asylums, fire alarm systems, 1704.5(e)
Atomic energy, Federal Regulations, 703.2
Auditoria, ventilation, 1207.9(c)
Automotive lifts, construction, 1800.10(c)
  permits, 1800.5
  plans, 1800.4
Automotive repair shops, 708.0
  boilers, 704.2(b)
  classification, 708.2
  heating equipment, 708.6
  Occupancy Classification, 302.1
  pits, 708.4(b)
  sprinkler system, 708.5
  ventilation, 708.4
Automotive service stations, 707.0
  classification, 707.2
  gasoline pumps, canopy, 707.4
    location, 707.4
  gasoline storage, 707.3
  heating equipment, 707.5
  Occupancy Classification, 302.1
Auxiliary spaces, stages, see Stages,
  auxiliary spaces
Awnings, canvas, 503.6(j)
  slow-burning plastic, 503.6(j)
Axial loads, pile foundations, allowable,
  1107.1

public supply, 1600.6(e)(2), 1601.1
storm, disposal, 1600.6(k)
supply requirements, 1600.6(b)
well, 1600.6(f)
Water-cement ratio, method I concrete,
1004.3(a)(2)
method II concrete, 1104.3(b)(3)(a)
Water circulation, swimming pools, 715.5
Water closet compartments, mechanical
ventilation, 1206.4(c)
Water conservation, 1600.6(c)
Water curtain, for stages in places of assembly, 802.2(b)(7)b
Waterfront property, Occupancy Certificates.
121.4
Waterproofing, pit, 1412.3(b)
Water spray nozzles, at conveyor openings,
504.4(b)
Water supply, cross-connection, 1601.3(a)
sprinkler systems, see Sprinkler systems,
water supply
standpipe systems, see Standpipe system,
water supply testing, 1606.4(c)
Water tanks, 503.8(h)
Water towers, Inside Fire Districts, 403.2(g)
Walkways, construction, lighting, 1901.4
swimming pools, 715.2(a)
temporary, 1901.5(e)
Wall openings, exterior, Table 3-5, 503.1(a)
Wall signs, 717.8(a)
Walls, adjoining, protection of, 1902.1(c)
exterior, open parking structures, 710.4
foundation, 1105.0
horizontal loads, 906.1(d)
Window hardware, 604.4(j)
masonry, 1901.6(a)(12)
party, fire-resistance rating, 503.2
shear, load distribution, 906.2(a)
stud, 1006.6(a)
swimming pools, 715.2(a)
Warning lights, see Warning signs
Warning signs, 1901.7, 1909.1(c)
red lanterns, 1901.7(a)
red lights, 1901.7(a)
walkways, 1901.4
Welding, aluminum, 1007.3(b)

steel, 1004.3(b)
Well water, 1600.6(f)
Window boarding, demolition operations,
1905.1(c)(2)
Windows, bay, 503.6
in shafts, 504.5(b)
openable, locks, 604.4(j)(2)c
oriel, 503.6
stair enclosures, 604.8(j)
Wind loads, 904.0
Wire cable, 1010.2, 1909.2(b)
fittings, 1010.6
protection, 1010.8
Wire rope, 1909.2(b)
loading, 1907.4(d)
Wires, embedment in fire protection,
502.0(a)
Wood, 1006.0
empirical provisions, 1006.6
firecutting, 1006.5(a)
fire-retardant, see Fire-retardant wood
floors, 1006.6(c)
identification, 1006.2
inspection requirements, Table 10-1, 10-2
non-stress grade, 1006.3
protection of members, 1006.5(b)
quality control, 1006.4
structural design, 1006.0
stud walls, 1006.6(a)
Wood beams, notches, 1006.6(c)(3)
Wood construction, 1006.8
bracing, 1006.6(b)
bridging, 1006.6(c)(2)
floors, 1006.7(a)(2)
nailing schedule, 1006.6(d)
sheathing, 1006.6(b)(1)
Wood footings, 1105.2(a)
Wood partitions, 1006.6(a)
Work shops, 802.2(b)(11)

X-ray machines, 703.4

Yard hydrants, 1702.2
required, 1702.2
with special equipment, 1702.2(f)
Yard main, private, 1702.14(b)(2)